SOUTHERN · TIMES ·

Contents

We regret but availability of space has precluded the inclusion of all we had promised and similarity intended for this issue including 'From the Footplate'.

The next issue of Southern Times, No 7, will definitely contain: the N15X rebuilds, Oxted Part , **SCT**'s images of Bulleid Pacifics, Observations at Farnborough, Treasures from the Bluebell Museum, From the Footplate and whatever else we can shoehorn in! We promise something for everyone.

The Transport Treasury

TIMES SERIES

Front Cover: A1X No 32678 at work on the short line to the breakwater at Newhaven. This siding was used for taking building materials to maintain the sea defences and survived as late as August 1963. *Gerald Daniels*

Above: Enthusiasm or madness at Rolvenden? The Branch Line Society Kent & East Sussex Light Railway Tour of 12 April 1958. This was an afternoon event with a Hastings DEMU used between Charing Cross and Robertsbridge (and later return) and at which point there was a change into locomotive hauled stock top and tailed by AIX tanks Nos 32636 and 32678. On the outward journey from Robertsbridge to Tenterden Town stops were made at all stations and halts, six minutes between allowed at Rolvenden although it is not completely clear if in the above view the participants are attempting to 'escape' or return! *Gerald Daniels / Transport Treasury*

Rear cover: A royal 'Hornby'! Bulleid / Raworth electric No 20001 perhaps fresh from overhaul, certainly at least freshly repainted - just look at those shoe beams - in charge of an unreported working. Can anyone advise please? *Gerald Daniels*

Copies of many of the images within **SOUTHERN TIMES** are available for purchase / download.

In addition the Transport Treasury Archive contains tens of thousands of other UK, Irish and some European railway photographs.

© Kevin Robertson. Images (unless credited otherwise) and design The Transport Treasury 2023

ISBN 978-1-913251-55-0

First Published in 2023 by Transport Treasury Publishing Ltd.,
16 Highworth Close, High Wycombe, HP13 7PJ

www.ttpublishing.co.uk or for editorial issues and contributions email to southerntimes@email.com

Printed in the Malta by the Gutenberg Press.

The copyright holders hereby give notice that all rights to this work are reserved.
Aside from brief passages for the purpose of review, no part of this work may be reproduced,
copied by electronic or other means, or otherwise stored in any information storage and
retrieval system without written permission from the Publisher.

This includes the illustrations herein which shall remain the copyright of the respective copyright holder.

INTRODUCTION

One of the joys of holding the privileged position of Editor is the sheer number of individuals who are regularly in touch offering material and making suggestions. Aside from the opportunity to see items that might otherwise be lost it is comforting to appreciate that whilst the Southern Railway may already be fast approaching its 80 year demise, interest remains as strong as ever.

I recall years ago from a particular favourite television series 'Porterhouse Blue' - if you have not seen it, satirical humour at its best - a quote along the lines that so many suffer from the 'British disease', referring to our propensity to look backwards and not forwards.

Well I for one are proud to acknowledge I do just that, wanting to learn ever more about what I never saw, do not recall clearly enough, and in many cases wish I had seen,

That is not to say I loath the present, far from it, but I hope I use what for me is the most suitable of the new technology but certainly without the desire to clamber over my neighbour and so have the doubtful kudos of owning the latest gadget or whatever.

I mention this for whilst I pen this piece on a warm late May day, the spectre of 'Artificial Intelligence' looms high in the news. Will it affect me, should I be concerned? At the moment I hope not; I promise it is the below named who is genuinely penning this missive, although I have conducted a small experiment of my own. I asked an 'AI bot' to write 100 words on the LBSCR 'K' class engines and which readers will note is our featured class in this issue. 'AI bot' did it very well, the text was received within a few seconds, grammatically correct but as I discovered with one major factual flaw; it was stated that an engine of this class was preserved at the National Railway Museum. Sadly we know that not to be the case as none survived but it does prove the point, somewhere on the internet, and of course this is where 'AI bot' trawls for information, there is a false entry. Of course any computer is only ever as good as the information that is in-putted in the first place, so we hope this is just a momentary slip. Otherwise I have to say I was impressed, especially as asking the same question a few moments later came up with a totally different set of words although again with the same error. Be assured, (I hope not depressed) if we ever do use 'AI' in 'ST' and there are NO plans to do so in the foreseeable future we will advise accordingly; in exactly the same way if we publish a b/w image that has been colourised in the 21st century.

Perhaps I am in awe in the same ways our fore-bearers were with the new technology of their period and which we now look back on without comment simply taking it all for granted.

That technology might well have started with the railway infrastructure, the bridges the almost Gothic styling of some of the principal stations, and then the ever larger locomotives, the speed, the associated technology; the telegraph, 'railway time' and so on.

Today the steam engine is considered a museum piece (fortunately kept alive by that dedicated band of volunteers on the various heritage lines), and yet a century ago it was some of the best brains in the country who were developing and modernising the Southern Railway (amongst others) those same brains, and similarly the directors, recognising that to survive in business one has to innovate and move forward. We cannot stand still.

It remains exactly the same today, we innovate to move forward. Perhaps not exactly the same way the SR did years before where a most definite 'learn from the past and re-use and re-purpose the old for the present' was the motto.

I have a friend who in the past was involved in the commissioning of new trains for the current day South Western network. I will not mention his name although suffice to say some of the horror stories I hear reference their (lack of) reliability leave me feeling cold for the future. Perhaps 'AI' would have been useful with these sets.

So is AI a threat to our hobbies and interests? I sincerely hope not. Here at Southern Times we have always attempted to incorporate some material which is new, which is not on the internet and which is the result of original research. This is balanced with recalling the past where necessary and in a way which we hope creates additional interest.

AI may be able to string words together but it cannot locate images that are not freely available. I intend to continue the sourcing and including examples of the old together with including readily accessible material. After all none of us can ever hope to be able to identify every website, source or library where material on our particular interest may repose.

I hope you will continue to be with me as we venture forward into the past.

Kevin Robertson

Some readers may well be familiar with the books I compiled a few years on 'Wartime Southern'. At the time I honestly believed there would be few if any others to come but from a different source a new batch has arrived - some clearly damaged from exposure to light / heat / water even but many still worth including and clearly indicating the difficulties and trauma the Southern railway suffered at this time. Indeed we might even pause a while to consider how they did manage to keep train running - but this they did and all credit to all concerned.

None were identified by any annotation of any sort and so it was very much a detective exercise together with a 'help' to friends and colleagues for others. Many thanks to all concerned.

We start opposite top and opposite bottom at Cow Lane Bridge, Peckham. The collapse of this bridge was the result of enemy action over night on 10/11 May 1941. The Peckham Rye - Nunhead / Queens Road (Peckham) routes blocked as a result. Notwithstanding the damage seen, both slow lines were reopened running over a temporary structure in just 36hrs. and subject to a 5mph restriction. Further repairs enabled the Catford loop lines re opened in just five days.

Above - Damage assessment at West Dulwich. This location was subjected to enemy attach on several occasions; including on 14 September 1940; 4 February and 7 July 1944. The above view is thought to date from July 1944 the wooden platform shredded like matchwood.

Left: West Croydon and the effect of a flying bomb that hit on 23 June 1944. If there was any good fortune involved it was that the hit came at 2.00am although the damage to the station, both signal boxes and EMU empty stock was considerable. Unfortunately there were three fatalities, one signalman and two other railway staff.

The barrage continued elsewhere and at 7.00am a further missile fell in what was referred to as 'C' section at Norwood Down Yard.

This one was very destructive, blasting the passing 6.10am Three Bridges to London Bridge EMU on which 56 passengers were injured (15 seriously). In addition the engine and a train of 39 wagons and brake-van, together with parts of the Down Yard and more wagons were damaged, three men being sent home with shock.

A few minuets later at 7.05am another missile fell followed by a third at 7.25am. This last pair fell close to Hither Green Station, one on either side: two waiting passengers and five staff were injured; three three-car and two four-car EMU, one W&C car, seven luggage vans and five wagons were damaged.

This page: Damaged EMU stock, location not confirmed, and with recovery work taking place.

Above: Formal SR records of the time indicate Charlton station and the services through it were affected several times. The first was in September 1940 when an unexploded bomb caused a cessation of services between here at Woolwich Dockyard for four days. Further UXB problems affected services to Blackheath shortly afterwards, The devastation seen here was the result of a V1 flying bomb that hit the station at 3.00pm on 23 June 1944. Impact was made with the up platform and the station house demolished: three waiting passengers were killed, plus the signalman's wife in the house and three staff were injured. The lines were blocked for 27 hours and the station closed until 6 July. In the interim North Kent line trains were diverted via Bexleyheath, those to Dartford only being diverted at Perry Street Junction to Abbey Wood and back, with passengers for Dartford to Plumstead inclusive having to use buses.

Opposite: Ashford, Kent. As a prime railway centre Ashford was a certain target for the enemy and not surprisingly the location features in the records on several occasions. The first mention was on 17 July 1940 when high explosive fell on the works. Twelve workers were injured although in the nearby New Town residential area there were two fatalities and a further two injuries. (We might mention that on what is regarded as the crucial day of the Battle of Britain 15 September 1940, a Hurricane fighter crashed on to the Tonbridge to Ashford main line at Staplehurst both lines being blocked. Even so the debris was cleared and normal working restored in just 30 minutes.) On the same day further high explosive fell on the works, railway staff were again fortunate with just five injuries although once more there were fatalities outside, this time three persons in nearby railway cottages. The saw mill at the works was also hit on at least two other occasions whilst at 4.30pm on 28 October 1940 bombs fell on the Erecting and Machine Shops; this time seven men and one woman were killed and 14 workers injured, also four locomotives (not detailed) were damaged..It is believed further damage may have been caused by a hit at some point in late 1942 but no information is available.

The photographs opposite are show devastation believed caused by a flying bomb which struck at 6.50pm on 16 August 1944. Aside from the obvious damage to the signal box, several wagons were damaged in the cripple sidings. The signalman and two other staff were taken to hospital. Traffic continued to be was handled but without the assistance of telegraph or telephone communication for nearly 24 hours).

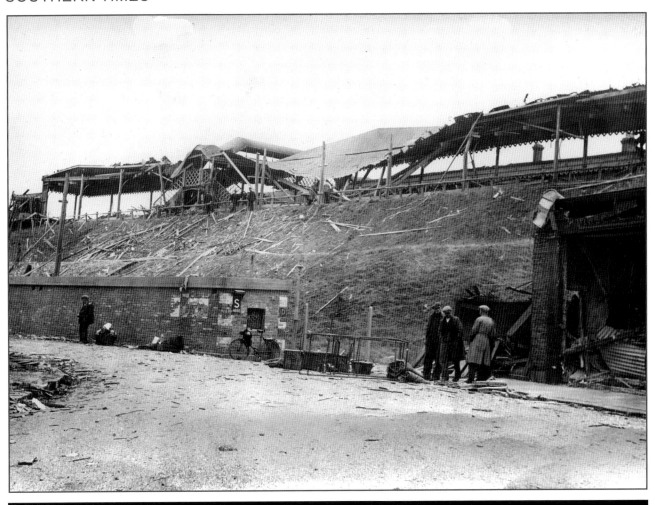

Another location to suffer badly was at Hither Green; another strategically important location so far as the railway was concerned. Matters first come to note with the extremely unfortunate explosion of a delayed action bomb in the subway of the station at 5.45pm on 11 September 1940. The device believed to have been dropped in consequence of a raid around 4.00pm the same day. One railwayman and five passengers were seriously injured. The yard and locomotive shed were closed when wagons containing explosives were set on fire and two exploded. Yard Master Savage was awarded the George Medal for his bravery on this occasion. The citation paraphrased "As one of a consignment of 10 wagons marked 'Explosives' was burning, Mr. Savage rallied the available staff for fire fighting, quickly arranged for the wagon to be isolated and with a stirrup pump he crawled underneath with the hose and successfully attacked the fire. His efforts had a splendid effect upon the staff and although the propellant charge caught fire and exploded, in putting out the flames he stopped what would otherwise have been a very disastrous explosion. When questioned afterwards by the Divisional Superintendent about the names of the men who took part, Savage did not mention himself and his actions only came to light later." Further extensive damage was caused to the sidings at Hither Green on 13 October 1940; the yards here also hit on at least two further occasions later.

In the period of the flying bombs of 1944, at 2.30am on 16 June a V1 fell in Hither Green Sidings damaging six roads, a locomotive, C 0-6-0 No. 1593, 46 wagons and four brake-vans; extensive damage was done as well to buildings and two staff were injured, but all roads were clear in 18 hours. A further missile at 7.05am and another at 7.25am fell close to Hither Green Station, one on either side: two waiting passengers and five staff were injured; three three-car and two four-car EMU, one W&C car, seven luggage vans and five wagons were damaged. All communications were interrupted and both Dartford Loop lines and the up through line were blocked, for respectively 9½ and 2½ hours.

Hither Green B box smashed at 4.50pm on 12 July, 1944. Another flying bomb wreaked havoc on 27 October; it fell close to Hither Green Yard at 11.45pm damaging some buildings, five brake-vans and several wagons, also injuring three staff

Just five days later in the early hours of 2 November another missile made a very large crater in Hither Green Yard, doing extensive damage to track, buildings and nearly 100 wagons. Seven staff were injured and four disabled by shock. All communications between

Hither Green Sidings 'B' and 'C' Boxes were severed and trains operated by time interval working for 6 – 9 hours

Opposite top: The consequences of enemy action at an unknown location - does a reader recognise the location perhaps from the background? We decided to include this view on the basis of the wagons, perhaps especially the box van; tossed around as if it were a toy and yet even empty having a tare weight of perhaps 12 tons. Of interest too are the bicycle type luggage carts. From this we may deduce they were used for local deliveries and with several apparent and perhaps not having suffered seemingly much damage, might this have been a major goods depot?

Opposite bottom: New Cross Yard signal box devastated by blast and shrapnel, although not confirmed this was likely to have been the result of a missile falling at 4.45am on 21 July 1944.. (Records show that in the early afternoon of 1 August the station was damaged internally '...with tickets strewn everywhere...'.)

Above: Wimbledon car sheds after a flying bomb hit on 4 July 1944.

Aside from the human cost already mentioned, the following report filed in the Southern Railway Estate Department may be cited as a poignant reminder of what could happen although the location of the building concerned is not mentioned: "Living at Flat No. 166: G. Crawley, Caretaker for the Estate Dept., has lost his home completely. His son has died of his injuries; his wife and daughter (3½) are all right, and have moved to the other caretaker's (intact) flat. Flat 176: G.T. Eyles, platelayer – his wife is killed and he is in hospital badly injured. Flat 175: W.C. Cousins, guard (Hither Green), has lost his wife and son (14) killed, home completely destroyed. Flat 180: W.G. Gower, pensioner platelayer, he and his wife in hospital badly injured and their home destroyed. Flat 185: S. Sivyer, is in the Forces, but his wife and young child are in hospital badly injured. Flat 201: A. Morgan, foreman (B. Arms), killed with his wife. Flat 206: N. Brusey, painter (Engineering Dept.), is in the Forces but his wife is killed and home destroyed. Flat 225: E.W. Sell, ticket collector, home destroyed. Flat 227: C.J. Wiseman, fireman (New Cross), all right, but home destroyed. Flat 230: porter (B. Arms), home destroyed."

Newhaven Reflections
Howard Cook

Whilst considering ferry ports within ex-Southern Railway territory, one name rarely at the top of anybody's list would be Newhaven. Cross-Channel services from this modest East Sussex port have been connected by rail since 1847 when the London, Brighton and South Coast Railway opened a terminal called Newhaven Wharf, the line from Lewes being later extended through to Seaford in 1864. The adjacent ferry terminal however was affected by tide times so by reclaiming land south of Mill Creek, a better-situated station was opened on 17 May 1886 when the original 1847 station was re-named Newhaven Harbour and the new terminus rather confusingly acquiring the title of Newhaven Harbour (Boat Station). This title was retained until re-named Newhaven Marine on 14 May 1984, the day the final boat train operated from this station.

Above - Viewed southwards from Harbour station footbridge, the through line to Seaford diverges left whilst the approach to Marine is via the third track from the right. The quayside line to the far right is predominantly used for parcels and goods with direct access to ferries. Mill Creek can be clearly identified above the signal gantry as can the cliff and fort on the right-hand side of the picture, hovering above West Quay on the opposite side of the River Ouse. Photo dated 12 September 1967.

Opposite top - Historically, Newhaven has always been a dumping ground for withdrawn rolling stock and on 22 April 1961 Brighton-based 2F Class C 0-6-0 No. 31280, a Wainwright SECR design, is captured arriving with a rake of condemned coach underframes for scrapping.

Opposite bottom - Amongst other wooden-bodied rolling stock awaiting burning on 22 April 1961 is ex-Departmental 'Birdcage' brake No. DS26, believed to have been built between 1909 and 1910 for the SECR by Metropolitan Amalgamated RC&W Works, Saltley, Birmingham (later Metro Cammell). The term 'birdcage' derives from the barred window in the guard's raised lookout window whilst the composite 2nd/3rd class compartment accommodation was originally served by separate lavatories for each class.

Marine station struggled on for a few years but was allowed to deteriorate with the condition of the roof being of particular concern. Due to safety concerns the station was unofficially closed to the public in August 2006 meaning British Rail had to operate a daily 'parliamentary service' to uphold its legal obligation for an open station. This involved the extension of one evening service along the short distance from Harbour station into the terminus whence it stopped and reversed back whilst being inaccessible to any intending passengers, probably only railway enthusiasts! The service was advertised however, with ticket-holders offered a complimentary taxi for the short transfer. In May 2017 the buildings were finally demolished, the service suspended under a re-signalling scheme and the station officially closed on 22 October 2020. Bringing the tale right up to date I am advised the 21.11 Brighton – Newhaven Harbour still runs with ecs in and out of the old Marine station but not advertised for passengers. This is shown in the Working Timetable as 5C69 21.44 Harbour – Marine and 2C69 21.58 Marine – Brighton.

Another curiosity about Marine is that its single platform was numbered 3, harping back to its days as an effective extension of Harbour station whose platforms 1 and 2 served, as they do now, the branch to Seaford. A contact, who shall remain nameless, visited Marine one night to try to ride the 'ghost train' but found the site surrounded by fencing. A harbour security officer reluctantly granted access but unfortunately the train crew were not so accommodating!

The LB&SCR's fierce rivalry with the South Eastern Railway created the desire for this cross-Channel route proclaiming the journey from London to Paris as the most direct as the rail journey to the port is shorter than the SER's to Dover, albeit the sea crossing to Dieppe being far longer and more prone to adverse weather. Regardless, both ports still operate ferries despite the opening of the Channel Tunnel in 1994. Regrettably, named boat trains are a thing of the past but historically various services have operated to connect with sailings, mainly from London but also from further north and indeed Scotland.

Of course Newhaven is not just a ferry port and commercial activities were increased accordingly by the Newhaven Harbour Company alongside passenger improvements. The major expansion was in 1878 when the LB&SCR instructed the construction of new quays, seawall, entrance piers and the lighthouse as well as a concrete breakwater extending 730 metres into the sea. The East Side land reclamation from the afore-mentioned Mill Creek also created new land which created a base for many industries associated with the port. Further improvements were made by straightening the River Ouse wall in 1938 and, during both World Wars, the port was very strategic for the movement of troops and material to and from the Continent, being closed to the public for long periods and designated a 'Special Military Area'. Accordingly the railway sidings were enlarged along with port facilities and fortifications whilst large numbers of men were stationed in the area.

Not too far north of Harbour station is Newhaven Town which serves the main community. Beyond that remains the once notorious level crossing on the A27 coast road, the scene of many lengthy delays before the by-pass flyover was constructed to replace the old iron swing bridge over the river, which ceased operation in 1974. The bridge over the Ouse also carried the West Quay Tramway down to the harbour. This fascinating line closed in August 1963 and attracted many photographers whilst in operation. Over the tramway sections, goods trains were preceded by the pedestrian shunter bearing a red flag. One such 'celebrity' from the 1930s was Harry Avis who is well-documented in the local history museum, besides giving his name to a trading estate and Avis Road.

Opposite - Marsh/Billinton Class H2 4P No. 2422 *North Foreland* is seen shunting empty stock on Newhaven East Side having arrived with a Down boat train on 6 August 1939, a month prior to the commencement of hostilities with Germany. Built at Brighton Works in 1911, these 4-4-2s were an instant success on London – Brighton expresses including the elite Pullman services, the 'Brighton Limited' and the 'Southern Belle'. Like the Class H1, the H2s were mainly stored during WWII as a result of the cessation of ferry services but returned to service in peace time and continued operating boat trains until October 1956. The final survivor, as No. 32424, lasted until April 1958 as something of a celebrity locomotive but pleasingly, a replica of *Beachy Head* is currently being constructed at the Bluebell Railway, utilising many existing components.

Right - Stroudley 'Terrier' Class A1X 0-6-0T heading a short transfer goods on 26 August 1961 across the river Ouse swing bridge from the West Quay branch to North Quay. Built in 1875, No. 62 *Martello* started life on London suburban duties based at New Cross. Shortly before closure of the West Quay branch it was reallocated to Eastleigh to see out the final days of the Hayling Island branch and spared scrapping by becoming an open-air exhibit at Butlin's Holiday Camp near Ayr before its preservation was secured at Bressingham Steam Museum where it now carries the LB&SCR number B662.

Bottom - 0464 Northampton-based Stanier Class 5MT 4-6-0 No. 45398 is recorded reversing back past Newhaven Town signal box on 19 August 1964 having arrived with the Glasgow – Newhaven 'Continental' car sleeper train. Whilst expensive, these summer-only trains were a success until the quality of cars improved and the motorway network was completed. The same journey today takes over 12 hours, entails 4 to 5 changes and costs a little over £141 single but with no car carrier service.

Receiving routine attention outside Newhaven engine shed on 31 July 1954 is L. Billinton Class K 4P5F 2-6-0 No. 32353 allocated to Three Bridges, alongside Maunsell 'Schools' V class 4-4-0 No. 30915 *Brighton*, a Stewarts Lane resident having arrived with a boat train, as indicated by its disc code. The residents of this Brighton sub-shed would deal with local freight and shunting duties whilst much of the activity of the depot would be concentrated on turning and servicing visiting locomotives.

Stabled between duties outside Newhaven shed on 25 August 1961 are a pair of Brighton-based Billinton Class E4 0-6-2Ts, Nos. 32503 and 32479. Under British Railways, Newhaven (NHN) depot was designated a sub-shed of 75A Brighton (BTN until 1950) and no longer had a dedicated allocation of locomotives.

Even more obscure though is the East Quay line which ran along the Sussex coastline from Newhaven to Tidemills and almost Seaford. Odd traces of this remain embedded in path crossings whilst the actual alignment is almost untraceable. This line was used by BR for many years for trains to dump PW ballast etc. after weekend engineering works. There is a story concerning the signalman who manned the box at Southease who rang the Special Traffic Office at Croydon to complain about the timing of one of these workings as it was due to pass his box at the same time as he usually fed his goats and other animals. The clerk involved for some reason took pity on him and re-timed the train to stand in Haywards Heath Down sidings for 30 minutes to allow the feeding to go uninterrupted. The train crew were none too pleased with Control but at least it ensured they made the train keep to time.

Finally it should not be forgotten that Newhaven once had a 4-road engine shed (sub of 75A Brighton) situated immediately south of the road/rail swing bridge on the east bank, from where numerous sidings extended southwards, more recently used for storing surplus rolling stock. The duties from this depot comprised mainly shunting and local trip workings but more powerful motive power could often be found on shed for servicing, having arrived with boat trains or other special workings.

There is still much to be seen of railway interest in this outpost of the Southern but sadly the days of Terriers, Atlantics and Hornbys are long gone. However, through the good offices of the Transport Treasury, we are able to offer a fine selection of pictures recorded for posterity by forward-thinking photographers over the years.

There is still much to be seen of railway interest in this outpost of the Southern but sadly the days of Terriers, Atlantics and Hornbys are long gone. However, through the good offices of the Transport Treasury, we are able to offer a fine selection of pictures recorded for posterity by forward-thinking photographers over the years. Here BR dual voltage electric Bo-Bo (later Class 71) No E5017 is observed negotiating the notorious level crossing outside Newhaven Town station with a service from Victoria on 27 July 1966. Although the crossing remains open for local road traffic, the congestion has been significantly relieved by the construction of an elevated by-pass just to the north of this location.

On 12 July 1967 BR Class 73 electro-diesel Bo-Bo No. 73124 passes through the Harbour station over the harbour road crossing on the approach to Newhaven Marine with the Down 'Continental' boat train, correctly displaying headcode '76' for boat trains over this route. Few would have guessed at the time that 56 years on, 27 members of this versatile class still operate on the network, albeit in entirely different roles.

Southern Region samples 1960-1972
From the collection of Roger Geech

Setting aside commercial organisations and the national railway societies, one of the most prolific organisations in organising railtours in the 1950s and 1960s was the Railway Enthusiasts Club of Farnborough - and still running as a club today. Their heyday for tours was very much in the years before branch and line closures with regular outings organised both local and national.

One of these type of special were the half-day tours such as took place on 15 October 1960 starting and finishing at Farnborough taking in the Aldershot Government siding, the Bentley to Bordon branch and the stub ends of both the Basingstoke and Alton and Meon Valley lines from Alton. Originally referred to as the 'North Hampshireman' the special was far better known as the 'Aldershot Area Rail Tour'. Motive power was M7 No 30028 with capacity limited to pull-push set No 1 consisting of two coaches. Departing at 2.05 pm from Farnborough photo stops were made at varying points. The special is seen below traversing the Borden branch.

Opposite - On the racing stretch between Basingstoke and Woking, we have an original light pacific on a Salisbury line working. Stopping services to and from Salisbury continued to be steam hauled up to the time steam was abolished in July 1967. Plans to electrify the section between Basingstoke and Salisbury - and presumably then back from Salisbury to Eastleigh and Southampton - have been on and off the cards several times, in consequence of which Salisbury services are often seen as the poor relation.

We also see a rebuilt pacific powering through Brookwood in the early 1960s at which time in was only the slow lines between Woking and Pirbright Junction which were energised. Brookwood had once been the junction for the Necropolis line into Brookwood cemetery and on the opposite side the short branch to Bisley. Traces of the Necropolis line junction disappeared many years ago but certainly well into the 1960s it was possible to view the steep route and girder bridge which once carried the Bisley branch down and for a short distance parallel to the up side lines.

20

Opposite top - Last knockings for the Bordon branch from Bentley. The date was 9 January 1966 when the LCGB organised their 'S15 Commemorative Tour' from Waterloo to Eastleigh and return, the outward journey pausing at Bentley for 'U' No 31639 to take the special the short distance to and from Bordon, possibly also the very last passenger train to traverse the branch which closed completely on 4 April 1966, regular passenger workings having been withdrawn almost nine years earlier on 16 September 1957. The train is see here at Bentley with S15 , No 30837 in charge.

Opposite bottom - Another special two months later was on 20 March 1966 organised this time by the RCTS. This was again a round trip from and to Waterloo with a variety of motive power. Leaving Waterloo and running as far as Salisbury was No 34089 *602 Squadron*, the train banked out of Waterloo by No 80154. At Salisbury there was a reversal with No 75070 taking the special via Redbridge to the Ocean Terminal within the Eastern Docks at Southampton. After this a pair of USA tanks, Nos 30064 ans 30073 were used for a run to Fawley and back thence to Southampton Terminus where No 75070 again coupled on to Fareham. The final branch visited was from Fareham to Gosport, the line having lost its passenger service in 1953 and for some years held the dubious distinction of being the largest town in England without a railway connection. At Fareham No 31639 replaced the Standard 4 both engines finally coming together again for the last leg back from Fareham via Petersfield and the Guildford new line, to Waterloo. The train is seen here on the viaducts at Fareham. Ten hours of rail travel which was exactly on time when returning to Waterloo.

Above - Southern engine, (former) Western shed. This is No 35022 previously carrying the name *Holland-Afrika Line* stands at the coaling stage at Weymouth on 27 May 1967. Steam had just six weeks left, No 35023 one of the remaining members of the class that would continue until the very end after which it was unceremoniously dumped and then scrapped in South Wales in April the following year. Coaling at Weymouth was by means of tubs, each holding half a ton of coal and first needing to filled by hand from a wagon and then tipped into the hungry tender below. No 35023 has almost certainly worked from Waterloo and is being serviced ready for a return working.

Exactly one month before the lower was taken and at the same location, No 34023 minus its *Blackmoor Vale* nameplates accelerates north soon to pass the former GWR engine shed at Weymouth on the right. No 34023 was destined to survive into preservation.

Friday 7 July 1967, No 35008, formerly carrying the name *Orient Line* gets away from Weymouth and with just 48hrs of potential service life left. Likewise the green Bulleid coaching stock behind, much of which would similarly become redundant at the same time.

Super power at Weymouth on 11 June 1967 for the Warwickshire Railway Society 'Farewell to Steam on the LSWR' tour. Two Merchant Navy pacifics, Nos 35013 and 35030; formerly carrying the names *Blue Funnel* and *Elder Demster Lines* are about to depart for Dorchester South where No 35013 will come off. The tour had started at Birmingham New Street, AC electric traction in the form of E3119 used as far as Willesden Mitre Bridge Junction where Nos 73085 and 34004 took over to Woking. No 34004 continued alone from Woking to Wareham where No 80146 was attached to the rear for a trip to Swanage. (The original itinerary had included the Lymington branch but engineering work at Winchfield necessitating single line working meant the original scheduled timings were not possible.) No 34004 continued alone from Wareham to the furthermost destination here at Weymouth. From Dorchester No 35030 took the train to Salisbury via Eastleigh where there was a reversal for No 34023 to continue to Basingstoke. At the latter point No 73085 was added the pairing taking the train to Willesden Junction and a transfer to electric traction (E3113).

An unusual location, Tilmanstone colliery in Kent, No 08 156 in charge of a rake of loaded wagons. Coal was mined from here until 1986.

25

Staines to Wokingham and beyond. Part 2
Jeremy Clark

A quarter-mile beyond Pooley Green the line comes to Egham, (21m 2ch). The station is situated to the south of the town centre, the building being on the Up side. It had a substantial two-storey brick structure incorporating accommodation for the stationmaster and a generous forecourt that also formed the goods yard. This consisted of four sidings, one of which passed through the large brick goods shed. In addition two stubs served side- and end-loading facilities which were augmented by a weighing machine and a crane. This was later superseded by a ten-ton capacity gantry crane to handle the heavy engineering output from the local works of Foster Wheeler, now an International organisation based in Switzerland with UK offices in Reading. The goods yard closed in January 1965 though the shed survived for many more years.

A long siding with a loop left the yard in the Down direction and curved to run to the head of Station Road to serve a corn warehouse. This probably belonged to J Bosher, a local coal and corn merchant with premises in the High Street and the station yard. No trace of either the siding or the warehouse exists.

The signal box stood on the Down side to the west of the crossing immediately beyond the platforms. The gates were replaced by barriers in December 1972 and the box ceased to be a block post from 8 September 1974: it was abolished six months later. The station building was replaced by a steel and glass structure opened in July 1985. A shelter in similar style was raised on the Down side in place of the South Western timber one. For the first time too a footbridge appeared between the platforms near the Up end of the new building, more convenient than either the level crossing or the original footbridge, also provided for general public use, alongside it.

In less than pristine condition, No 34077, formerly named *603 Squadron* is seen at Virginia Water on 5 February 1967. The headcode only tells us it is a Waterloo - Reading line service and not the working. Notice the AWS battery box on the front framing. *Alec Swain*

Three-quarters of a mile beyond Egham lies isolated Rusham crossing. The gate box here, on the Up side and backed by accommodation for the keeper, could be brought into use as a block post at busy times as, for example, when extra Ascot race traffic was running. Sparse road use justified conversion to an automatic half-barrier crossing in July 1966. From Rusham the line begins a near-seven mile climb to a summit at Drake & Mount's, formerly the site of a yard and sidings used by the business of that name for receipt, despatch and storage of building materials. Soon after Rusham comes Stroud or Stroude crossing – Stroude Road and village (pronounced Strood incidentally!) are to the east of the line – though it is now pedestrian-only and approached by tracks.

Virginia Water station is five chains short of 23¼ miles from Waterloo via Richmond with the junction of the Chertsey line at the Up end. The lake to which the station name refers is nearly 1½ to the west, in Windsor Great Park. It was created in 1753 by damming the small River Bourne, which eventually flows into the Thames at Chertsey, and became a very popular destination during the Victorian era, no doubt aided by the railway's arrival. The station itself, as noted earlier, was named Trotsworth for a short time but was renamed to advertise its proximity to the attraction. Nowadays the line is bounded to the west by the very select Wentworth Estate and its internationally-renowned golf courses. The estate was developed from 1923 by local builder W G Tarrant who had built the equally upmarket St George's Hill at Weybridge from 1911. Despite Tarrant's bankruptcy in 1931 his building business survived, construction at Wentworth continuing after World War 2.

In 1887 sidings were provided on the Down side approach to the station for coal traffic to St Ann's Heath Sanatorium, later the Holloway Sanatorium. This large mental hospital was funded mainly by philanthropist Thomas Holloway, who had made his money through patent medicines, or more particularly his flare for advertising them. (Most of the concoctions subjected to analysis after his death were found to have little medicinal value.) He also funded construction of Holloway College for women on Egham Hill. Both were designed with an exuberant finish by W H Crossland. Holloway did not see either of the buildings completed before his death in 1883. The College, now part of the University of London and prefixed 'Royal', was opened officially by Queen Victoria in June 1886. Building the Sanatorium started in 1873 but it did not finish until 1885. Following closure and a long period of neglect from the late-1960s its re-development began around 2000 into a gated residential estate, both within the

building itself and in the spacious grounds. The coal sidings had been taken out of use in 1963 though they remained in-situ for another quarter-century.

Virginia Water station has four platform faces and had an Up-side building reminiscent of Egham, two-storey accommodation for the stationmaster being incorporated in it. The main signal box, 'A' after Grouping, was on the Ascot line platform opposite the building and had a small waiting shelter beside it. The position and orientation of these suggest they were in place before the Chertsey line opened behind them. The B389 Virginia Water-Chertsey road bridges the station at the Up end with the footbridge between the platforms right alongside it.

The small goods yard, of two sidings only, was on the up side with connections at the Down end. Just beyond those connections the line bridged the meandering River Bourne as it made its way towards the Thames. The yard closed in May 1960 and now serves as the station car park. The station building was demolished to be replaced by a CLASP structure, then in vogue, in September 1973: it remains in use. The South Western ridged platform canopy gave way to a flat-roofed shelter from the same source. 'A' signal box closed a year later.

Sixteen chains beyond the extremity of the station the line met the east to south curve from the Chertsey route: Virginia Water 'B' box stood right by the junction on the Down side. The curve was taken out of use in July 1964, though it was to be another two years before 'B' box and its 'C' counterpart at the East junction on the Chertsey route were closed.

The line here is facing almost due south but now begins a long turn towards the west-north-west. Longcross (25m 11ch) is at the southernmost point of this curve in an isolated spot on Chobham Common. Opened with a Halt suffix in late-September 1942, its principal purpose was to serve the nearby MoD depot which was, and still is, a vehicle testing ground, oddly perhaps sited in a National nature reserve and an SSSI. Until relatively recently secrecy demanded Ordnance Survey maps showed no trace of the depot or the three-mile long testing track. Ironically too there is no vehicular access to the station. A siding trailing into the Down line from the depot was laid soon after the station opened. It lasted until November 1961. There never was a signal box here, the siding points presumably being worked by a ground frame. However, there were two block posts either side of the station, designed to break Up the 3¾-mile long section between Virginia Water and Sunningdale. Knowle East, closed in June 1969, was about ¾ mile toward Virginia Water and Knowle West a ¼ mile or so beyond Longcross. This box was taken out of use in July 1971. A Down siding was later put in near the site of Knowle East to receive aggregates and other material for the construction locally of the M3 motorway.

Until privatisation services calling here were few and far between. It was not unknown for a train due to stop there to go sailing through simply because the motorman was so used to doing so. A friend of mine, a now-retired driver, admitted doing just that, to be berated in no uncertain terms at Sunningdale by a woman who had wished to alight there. She was still at Sunningdale on his return trip from Reading, having apparently been carried helplessly to Virginia Water and then back to Sunningdale again – twice! I don't remember how the tale ended! Despite recent local developments and more trains calling the service is still irregular and the station remains one of the least used in the region. Longcross itself is about a mile south.

Sunningdale station is a little less than twenty-seven miles from Waterloo and, when opened, was about a mile south of the village which rests a little beyond the southern extremity of Windsor Great Park. One resulting oddity is that while the station just lies in Surrey the village is in Berkshire though the line crosses the County boundary only a couple of hundred yards further on. Nowadays housing development has spread out to meet the railway with a predominance of large and luxurious properties providing first Class business.

For five years, until 1873, the station was suffixed '& Bagshot' though it was to be five years after that the latter village acquired its own station with the opening of the line from Ascot to Ash Vale Junction in March 1878. The suffix '& Windlesham' lasted rather longer, from 1893 to 1920. (Google Maps still describe the station in this way!)

The main A30 road crosses the line at the Up end of the platforms but at an angle, which accounted for the particular massiveness of the gates. A footbridge was erected adjacent to the crossing in 1890. The road either side of the crossing was later widened but for safety reasons railed traffic islands were placed along the centre of the road on the approaches to the track. Thus half-barriers only were provided when the gates were replaced in 1970. The installation of full barriers took place shortly before the Feltham centre took over responsibility for signalling the station five years later. The signal box was on the Down side east of the crossing.

The pleasant single-storey station building with its low-ridge slated roof stood on the Up side overshadowed by the massive three-storey Station Hotel louring at it across the forecourt. The building was demolished in 1973 when the main entrance was moved to the Down side with the erection of a CLASP building. Like most such structures of this age it has not weathered well. A new footbridge close to it was provided at the same time. The hotel has also gone, its site now being occupied by a supermarket of rather less pretension.

The goods yard, behind the Down platform, became quite substantial with side-loading facilities enclosing one siding, which also had an end-loading dock, while two long sidings, one of which passed through the goods shed, spread out from the headshunt. A crane of 4½ tons capacity was provided later and the yard also contained a small gasholder, probably for station lighting. All traffic other than that for the coal merchants was withdrawn from the beginning of December 1965 and the yard closed completely in January 1969. It now forms the station car park.

A mile or so beyond Sunningdale the line reaches its summit in a cutting at Sunninghill, the high point being marked, as already noted, by private sidings owned by the building business of Drake & Mount. There were originally two sidings on the Up side here, one deep in the cutting to the west of the High Street overbridge, (B3020 Sunninghill-Windlesham road), possibly for facilitating loading sand dug from the cutting side. Drake & Mount's siding was to the east of the bridge and was probably in place from soon after the line's opening. The single siding, off a head shunt fed from a trailing connection in the Down line, was later augmented by two more. The site's facilities included a large goods shed and side- and end-loading banks. Another siding on the south side of the line was opened in 1900 to serve the works of the Ascot & District Gas & Electricity Company. It is probable the signal box here, situated close to where the Down siding joined the Down line, was opened at the same time. One of the two large gasholders in use before the First World War remains on the site, which closed in 1965. Drake & Mount's had ceased rail operation here four years beforehand.

Ascot lies one chain short of twenty-nine miles from Waterloo. The original two-platform station was much rebuilt and extended when the Ash Vale line opened in 1878, with five platform faces being provided. The Up line from the Wokingham direction has a face on each side, both numbered '1'. Platforms are connected by a subway which also leads directly to a path to the racecourse. Until July 1921 the station was suffixed '& Sunninghill'.

WR No 7811 *Dunley Manor* is seen collecting empty coaching stock from the sidings at Bracknell ready for Ascot races, 17 June 1964.

The main entrance remains on the Up side, the building dating from 1877 though a fire in 1982 required major remedial work: it is still in use. Access to the goods yard, which had a head shunt and convergence with the Down line at the London end, was in the forecourt. A 50' turntable featured among the facilities there, superseding an earlier 40' one providing access to a small one-road loco shed. The turntable continued in use into Nationalisation for visiting locomotives, especially those heading Race Specials from other Regions, though it was lifted around 1964 and the pit later filled in. However, another loco facility at the opposite end of the station alongside the line to Ash Vale was approved in 1889. This also was a single-road shed to which two locomotives were normally allocated. It was constructed in timber with a ridged, slated roof and continued in use after Grouping, later becoming a sub-shed to Feltham. It had fallen out of use by the mid-1930s and closed in 1937, though demolition did not come about until 1969.

Meanwhile a goods shed was constructed on the site of the loco shed in the eastern yard. At its height this yard had four sidings, end- and side-loading facilities and a crane of four tons capacity. The yard was closed to all but coal traffic on 11 July 1966 and completely in January 1969. It is now the station car park.

From 1878 the layout was worked from three signal boxes. The one on the Up side to the east of the station, classified 'A' by the South Western, had responsibility for the junction of the Wokingham and Ash Vale lines and the points into the goods yard. Those to the west were beyond the divergence of the two lines, both on the Up side of their respective routes. The one on the Ash Vale line was reduced to a ground frame in 1928: both West end boxes closed ten years later when a 'glasshouse' box labelled 'B' was commissioned on 16 October. In anticipation of electrification new connections at the Down end permitted Ash Vale line trains which, until the end of 1938 could only use platforms 4 and 5, to serve the other platforms as well. This change was made so that portions from/for the two destinations, Guildford and Reading, could be joined or divided here.

'B' box, situated off the Down end of the island platform 3 and 4, closed on 8 September 1974 when Feltham assumed its responsibilities. Further track changes took place at the same time, the three platform tracks that remain all now being reversible. There is an electrified siding on the trackbed between the former nos. 4 and 5 platforms with a siding off it that is no longer in use though an engineers siding –without third rail – lies parallel to it. In a throwback to former times the No 3 platform line provides access only to the Ash

Joining the line from Reading at Staines, ED No E6014 is coming off the Windsor line with a special working in 1965.

Vale route. This is a reflection of the general method of operation now, it being worked as a shuttle to/from Ascot off peak. One other change, a direct benefit of centrally controlled sliding doors, is that only those on the ticket office side of trains at platform 1 are opened.

A few hundred yards west of Ascot the Southern built a now demolished wooden platform against the Up line to increase capacity on race days. But Ascot West station, a mile onward from Ascot and just west of the A332 overbridge, was brought into use for race traffic in 1922 despite its position a mile from the course. It consisted of two platforms and a Down direction bay. By 1931 the bay had been converted into a siding with another laid parallel to it for use by Bertram Mills Circus, which had its winter quarters nearby. These sidings were taken out of use in July 1966.

A siding at the Down end leading off the bay line served a brickworks. Further sidings were laid off this end soon after the start of WW2 and by August 1943 had developed into four looped and three dead-end roads, though the lead out of the south end of the loops continued to the brickworks. Loco servicing facilities were later provided for engines off trains

bringing prisoners-of-war to a nearby camp. Most of the track had gone by 1951 though the MoD did not de-requisition the site for another ten years.

The very neat signal box was at the west end of the Down platform. It closed in October 1969 though the station had seen its last train four years previously. To this day, however, race traffic remains a staple of Ascot station, and when the Royal meeting is on morning suits, top hats, long flowing dresses and imaginative millinery can all be seen in quantity crossing the concourse at Waterloo and boarding Ascot-bound trains.

Martins Heron station stands just over thirty-one miles from Waterloo. It opened on 3 October 1988, a joint venture between BR and Berkshire County Council and placed to serve extensive nearby residential development. A supermarket is built on the Up side right alongside the line, the station's opening being a precondition for the supermarket's construction. The ticket office, a neat brick building under a ridge roof – a great improvement on the CLASP structures elsewhere on the line – is on the Up side with the footbridge close by. The Down side backs on to housing and open space.

A ¼-mile west of Martins Heron Feltham relinquishes signal control of the Down line to the 1933-built Wokingham box: the Up line boundary is three miles further west. In between lies Bracknell at 32¼ miles into the journey. This station and, indeed, its surroundings, have changed beyond all recognition since it opened. The original brick building on the Up side was a replica of Sunningdale with two-storey accommodation for the stationmaster incorporated in it. Very typical LSWR-style ridged canopies covered the platforms with the roofed footbridge towards the Up end. The signal box, also of typical South Western timber construction with outside framing, was on the country end of the Up platform close to the points into the goods yard. It survived, in Updated form, until 27 January 1974.

This was another station having a quite substantial goods yard with direct access to both Up and Down lines. It lay on the Up side at the country end and by the mid-1930s no fewer than nine sidings were available. One of these ended at a short side- and end-loading dock let into the rear of the Up platform while side-loading facilities adjoined three more of the sidings.

These ample loading facilities were also a reflection of the plentiful horsebox traffic using the station with its proximity to Ascot and local stables. A cattle dock and a crane of 7½ tons capacity were also provided while the large goods shed straddled one of the longer sidings. In addition there were two sidings on the Down side at the country end. The goods yard closed in January 1969.

The marked change in Bracknell's status stemmed from the decision taken by Government in 1949 to designate it as an overspill 'New Town' for London***. At that time the population was around five thousand, the plan being gradually to increase it fivefold. But within the widened boundaries of what is now Bracknell Forest Unitary Authority the estimated population in mid-2014 stood at just over 118,000. To meet the increasing travel demands put on the railway – though the considerable business and industrial development forming part of the town's planned growth was designed to restrict the need for commuting into London – 1975 saw the construction of a new station. This was built on the site of the existing one, temporary offices and platforms

2-EPB unit No 5679 on Waterloo-Weybridge service at Thorpe Lane crossing in 1965.

At the same crossing and almost certainly taken around the same time, it is a pair of 2-BIL sets with No 2052 leading that are seen. Thorpe Lane Crossing dated from 1896 and contained a frame of just eight levers with tappet locking. It closed in 1975.

being erected close by while the work was undertaken. The original platforms remained though both were extended, the Down one to the west and the Up one eastward beneath the Bagshot Road overbridge. The Up side station building is beneath a large office block while two small shelters were provided on the Down platform. An SR-type concrete footbridge superseded the covered LSWR one at the London end.

At thirty-four miles from Waterloo the line passes beneath the short Reading-Bracknell section of the A329 Virginia Water-Thames road built to motorway standard. Twenty-seven chains further on the control of the Up line is assumed by Wokingham box which is also responsible for one of the three level crossings in the next mile. There was a fourth at one time, Amen, closed at the end of August 1982 following the opening of the rerouted A329(M) which bridged the line. It had been equipped with half-barriers four years earlier. Just to the east of this crossing a siding led into the Binfield Brick & Tile Works on the Up side of the line. Bricks had been made in the Binfield area from the early

1800s with this company being active from the late-19th century. The siding closed in August 1965 though the works site was not cleared for redevelopment for another twenty years.

The first of the three crossings is Waterloo (35m 76ch) – named after the nearby Waterloo Lodge – which was equipped with automatic half-barriers in August 1965. Next comes Star Lane (35m 30ch), the crossing box here being a block post until mid-1957. Automatic half-barriers were installed in June 1964 but the subsequent sharp rise in traffic using it saw full barriers controlled from Wokingham installed. These came into operation in 1997. The third one, Smiths', a 'User Worked' foot crossing, lies a half-mile further on. Both Star Lane and Amen have been scenes of fatal accidents in recent years.

At 35m 35ch from Waterloo the line from Staines meets the ex-SER line from Guildford at Wokingham Junction, the distance by that route from its terminus at Charing Cross being no less than 61 miles and 72 chains.

Through train from Reading to Redhill via Guildford entering Wokingham in 1962. N class 2-6-0 No 31858 is in charge. Leaving the station, the service will take the right hand fork to travel via Farnborough North and Ash to Guildford before joining the line to Redhill south of Guildford.

Sixteen chains further on we reach Wokingham. The 1933-built signal box that has controlled the Staines line for the last few miles is on the Down side next to the level crossing at the Up end of the station.

As we have now arrived in former SER property, over which the SW&WR had running powers from its opening seven years after that of the RG&RR, no description follows. However, the station was scheduled for a complete year-long rebuild from Spring 2012. The featureless and time-worn CLASP structure erected in 1973 was superseded by the new building in October 2013.

The coming of electrification revolutionised local train services, not only in speed of journeys but in their frequency. A number changed their character too. For example, the presence of Sturt Lane Junction permitted circular Waterloo-Woking-Frimley-Ascot-Staines-Waterloo services in LSWR days, the 1890 timetable showing six in each direction on weekdays and two on Sundays. Similarly, in that year Staines West Curve carried five Windsor-Woking workings in both directions though at very odd intervals. As noted earlier Staines High Street was closed in 1916 though

regular passenger traffic had ceased to use the curve for some time beforehand. After Grouping very few Ash Vale line trains worked east of Ascot with Woking or Farnham being the southern terminating points. The change most marked by electrification was to be seen on this line where passengers from, say, Camberley found themselves with thirty-six direct trains to Waterloo rather than the two of steam days. Most of these were combined with Reading services joined/divided at Ascot. Similarly, until 1976 it was customary to combine Windsor and Weybridge portions east of Staines.

In 1982 through portions to Guildford via Camberley and Aldershot were withdrawn and a shuttle service to / from Ascot provided instead. From 1988 however, trains from Waterloo ran to Reading and Guildford alternately. This did not last and a reversion was made to the pre-1988 arrangement with Reading services now half-hourly off peak and Guildford shuttle connections provided at Ascot. The calling pattern has changed too. No longer do Reading/Guildford trains run non-stop between Waterloo and Staines as they once did but now call intermediately at Clapham Junction, Richmond, Twickenham and Feltham. Longcross continues to have an irregular service with a gap of more than three hours in the Down direction on weekday afternoons. Several journeys require a change at Ascot into a London-bound train. The Up direction is a mirror image with a long gap during the morning and a similar need to go to Ascot to get to Waterloo.

Stock in use is predominantly class 458 'Juniper' units working Waterloo-Reading and Ascot-Guildford services. They are also seen on Waterloo-Windsor and Waterloo-Hounslow-Chertsey-Weybridge trains supplemented by class 455 stock.

The lines discussed were the subject of yet more plans published in October 2008 for rail connections to Heathrow Airport from the south west of London. No fewer than ten studies and discussion documents for such a possibility had been aired since 1960, the 1984 one being the most fruitful in finally establishing the practicability of such connections, though they were based on a line into the airport from Feltham.

The 2008 proposals would have seen a rail line come southward from Terminal Five, crossing Stanwellmoor and Staines Moor to take Up the route of the closed Staines West branch, reconstruction of a new Staines High Street station, and reinstatement of Staines West curve. The estimated cost was put at £673m. The service to the airport was proposed to cover the routes Waterloo-Heathrow via Richmond and Staines, Guildford-Heathrow via Woking and Chertsey, and Reading-Heathrow via Wokingham and Bracknell. In all cases the service was based on two trains per hour each way, these being of a semi-fast nature calling at particular nodal points en route. Moreover, the proposal included extension of existing Heathrow Express services to a new terminal platform at Staines. Formal application was made to the Transport Secretary by BAA in July 2009 for authority to buy the necessary land and begin construction.

BAA claimed much support for the scheme but opposition was fierce with many Local Authorities and transport undertakings particularly voicing concern at potentially much-increased traffic delays at the many level crossings on these routes. The planned depot at Feltham, on part of the loco shed site in the former marshalling yard, raised environmental issues as did the crossing of Stanwellmoor through a site of special scientific interest.

In the event, and in the generally poor economic and financial situation of that year, BAA announced in April 2011 it was abandoning the scheme, citing the lack of Government investment and taking into consideration other ongoing capital requirements such as connections to Crossrail and HS2. However, in October 2011 Wandsworth Council outlined another proposal on much the same lines titled Airtrack-Lite. Once again the Staines West branch and the West Curve would feature in the proposal but exact details are lacking. Nevertheless, the probability of better and wider airport rail connections at some future date, particularly in the light of increasing road traffic and concomitant congestion around Heathrow as well as the prospect of a third runway, cannot be dismissed. In that respect the proposals of The Windsor Link Railway, which would have much less impact environmentally as well as on existing rail infrastructure, may yet provide a viable alternative to BAA's original scheme.

*The Shrewsbury & Chester Railway, a 'narrow' gauge line opened 4th December 1846, amalgamated with the GWR on 1st September 1854, the Amalgamation Act setting a 'mixing' precedent that was applied to subsequent amalgamations.

**In 1860 the OW&WR amalgamated with two other 'narrow' gauge railways, the Newport, Abergavenny & Hereford and the Worcester & Hereford, to form the West Midland, absorbed by the Great Western in 1863. The GWR had been involved with the OW&WR in competition with the L&NWR almost from its inception but one might safely infer this and earlier amalgamations heralded the coming death of the Broad Gauge thirty years later.

*** Others 'New Towns' forming a ring round the Capital were Basildon, Crawley, Harlow, Milton Keynes and Stevenage. Included in the plan but further afield were Peterborough, Corby and Northampton. Many existing towns, Basingstoke, Letchworth and the Kentish Ashford, for example, were set for enlargement.

Bibliography:

History of the Southern Railway, C F Dendy Marshall, revised by R W Kidner, Ian Allan Ltd., 1963.

Railways of the Southern Region, Geoffrey Body, Patrick Stephens Ltd., 1989.

Sir Herbert Walker's Southern Railway, C F Klapper, Ian Allan Ltd., 1973.

The London & South Western Railway, O S Nock, Ian Allan Ltd., 1965.

Waterloo to Windsor, Vic Mitchell and Keith Smith, Middleton Press, 1988.

S15 No 30448 at Pooley Green Crossing, Egham. *Neville Stead*

Branch Lines around Ascot, Vic Mitchell and Keith Smith, Middleton Press, 1989

Rail Centres: Reading, Laurence Waters, Ian Allan Ltd., 1990.

Railways Through the Thames Valley, C R L Coles, Ian Allan Ltd., 1982.

Official Ministry of Transport Report into accident at Staines, 6 January 1958.

An Historical Survey of Southern Sheds, Chris Hawkins and George Reeve, Oxford Publishing Co., 1979.

Pre-Grouping Railway Junction Diagrams 1914, Ian Allan Ltd., (undated).

British Railways Pre-Grouping Atlas & Gazetteer, Ian Allan Ltd., 1959.

Jowett's Railway Atlas of Great Britain & Ireland, Alan Jowett, Guild Publishing by arrangement with Patrick Stephens Ltd., 1989.

Railway Track Diagrams No 5, Southern & TfL, Ed by Gerald Jacobs, Quail Track Diagrams, TRACKmaps, 3rd edition, 2008.

TRACK atlas of Mainland Britain, 2009.

This article was inspired by and has drawn for much of the historical detail Upon one by John Spencer Gilks published in the November 1956 issue of The Railway Magazine.

Perusing the 'Net' provides innumerable possible sites of interest in the course of research. I have used this means for a number of confirmatory exercises as well seeking information on several non-railway subjects that appear in the article. Google Maps has been of particular assistance in illustrating the present state of stations that I am not familiar with or have not been able to visit personally.

Peering out at New Cross in early 1939 is No 2543.
R C Riley

The LBSCR, SR, and BR(S) 'K' class

It is perhaps customary to commence the description of a locomotive class from their inception, describing the design, build, work and finally demise.

This time we are going to break with tradition and instead deal with the demise at start, an end which came all too quickly and likely at the stroke of a red pen somewhere at Waterloo or even perhaps at BR headquarters at Marylebone.

Enter then the year 1962. The 17 engines of the K class were still at work and variously allocated to Brighton (8), Three Bridges (8), with one of the class engine possibly still at Redhill. (Different sources, all genuinely in their attempt to be accurate, tend to have slight variations in depot detail. The excellent 'BRDatabase site also has No 32351 shown as being at Bushbury in 1949.)

In November 1962 eight of the type were summarily laid aside with the remaining nine going by the end of December; possibly the last active member of the class being No 32341 which was noted on a Haywards Heath to Eastbourne van train on 28 December. The cull was even more surprising as three engines Nos, 32341/45 and 53 had all received general overhauls 12 or so months before.

It may then be appropriate to consider the reasons for this sudden cessation of work and which at the time was stated to be,'...the need to fulfil the Southern Region withdrawal programme'.

Backtrack one year from 1962 and we have the completion of Phase 2 of the Kent Coast Electrification Scheme and with the wholesale transfer of steam stock to the Western section. Additionally there was the now widespread use of the D65xx diesel type, whilst the third factor to be considered was the gradual reduction in locomotive numbers required in consequence of falling traffic and line closures.

We know that the various SECR 4-4-0s transferred to Nine Elms from the Kent area did little if any further useful work instead ending up stored at location such as Feltham; Nine Elms simply not having space. At the same time came an influx of Bulleid, Standard classes and Moguls, it thus made perfect sense to concentrate steam power in as few classes as possible. This then is likely to have been the reason for the rapid demise of

K class; along with the Lord Nelson, Schools, various Brighton tanks, W and Z classes, all of which went round the same time.

What was such a waste was the lack of forward planning or perhaps more accurately, the lack of cohesion between motive power and operations. Far too late now but it must be said yet another example of wasted money - on overhauls and similarly resources; surely it would have been better to use older engines to their limit before casting aside and so save money spent on maintaining newer stock destined for a longer fife.

That though was 1962 and should turn the clock back half a century from that time to circa 1912 and the LBSCR.

'The Brighton' along with its neighbours on either side was primarily a passenger railway, what freight there was limited but consisting of much coal, which was still the fuel of choice both for industry and domestic use.

Hauling such trains were the usually the C2X type of 0-6-0 tender engines, capable performers but sometimes lacking when it came to being able to keep their trains clear of the more intensive and speedier passenger workings. In consequence double heading was needed on occasions. A larger engine was needed and this was designed by Lawson Billinton as the 'K'.

An initial batch of five engines was ordered from Brighton with the first two, Nos 337 and 338 delivered in September and December 1913 respectively. The 338-341 were completed in 1914.

The two original engines were first based at the nearby running shed and put to work on main line freight duties. There is no doubt they were successful but at the expense of fire-throwing when worked hard and unsteady riding above 35mph.

Accordingly No 377 had modifications made to the blastpipe and the side control of the pony truck which resolved the issues. Similar modifications were then made to No 338.

The next three engines incorporated these modifications from new along with a slightly extended smoke box. Of the five, one No 341 was sent to New Cross with the remaining four based at Brighton.

A second batch of five engines was ordered even before the last of the original five had entered traffic but war constraints meant these were not delivered until 1916. War constraints also meant a simpler livery

was applied; plain black with yellow lettering. With ten engines now available the class were also now wider spread;

Brighton:	337 / 338 /339 / 340
Battersea:	342 / 343
New Cross:	341 / 344
Littlehampton:	345
Three Bridges:	346

Bradley recounts Billinton had the foresight to stockpile items including cylinder-blocks, tyres and other components to cover likely needs for several years ahead. By implication then this then refers to K class requirements but may well mean for other types also.

Top feed was fitted to Nos 345/6 which proved successful and had been retrospectively fitted to all the earlier engines by October 1920. A further modification to the feed water came when the clack boxes were contained within a second dome which came with the advantage of making boiler cleaning and inspections both easier and quicker.

During WW1 the class regularly handled 1,000 ton trains as well as troop specials bound for embarkation from Newhaven. Often these commenced at Three Bridges which was an interchange point with services arriving from The LNWR and GWR. The K would take over the train at this point, several of the class appearing at this location notwithstanding only one engine being official based here.

Post WW1 thoughts turned to further engines of similar type and a design was worked up for a tank engine variant with the 2-6-2T wheel arrangement. Possibly this had come about due to the difficulty in turning the K class on some of the turntables on the LBSCR system; Newhaven for example only being fitted with a 60' turntable in February 1917 whilst 45' turntables (albeit with extension gear) existed at Chichester, Eastbourne, Horsham, London Bridge and Tunbridge Wells. (A 'K' class engine and tender had a wheelbase of 47' 11".)

Allowing for the requirements of the civil engineer who also demanded a longer wheelbase, the maximum water capacity it was possible to achieve was 2,000 gallons, which compared unfavourably with the almost 4,000 gallons in a K class tender. The lower amount was considered insufficient and an order for n additional ten engines to the original design was substituted.

It was now that circumstances beyond the control of Billinton came into play. A further order for another 10 of the class was approved in April 1919 but this against

Doyen of the class No 337 photographed when new. (The right hand buffer is cut off on the original print.) The engine is seen here in photographic (dove) grey, lined in black and white, white lettering the latter shaded in black excepting on the buffer beam. Already this was the second livery to be carried as it had first run trials in all-over red oxide devoid of ownership details but identified with its buffer beam number. Following its portrait it was repainted in standard goods livery of gloss black with two lines of vermillion lettering. Transfer lettering and numbers were in yellow shaded in red and white.

Original No.	Later BR No.	Completed	Boiler fittings / cab cut-down.	Withdrawn	Final mileage
337	32337	Sept. 1913	Mar. 1937	Dec. 1962	987,434
338	32338	Dec. 1913	Apr. 1937	Dec. 1962	1,081,627
339	32339	Mar. 1914	Aug. 1936	Nov. 1962	974,541
340	32340	Jun. 1914	Sep. 1937	Dec. 1962	
341	32341	Nov. 1914	Jul. 1935	Dec. 1962	
342	32342	Oct. 1916	May. 1938	Dec. 1962	
343	34343	Nov. 1916	Aug. 1935	Dec. 1962	
344	32344	Dec. 1916	Oct. 1936	Nov. 1962	
345	32345	Dec. 1916	Jul. 1938	Dec. 1962	
346	32346	Dec. 1916	Sep. 1936	Nov. 1962	
347	32347	Dec. 1920	Jul. 1939	Dec. 1962	
348	32348	Dec. 1920	Jun. 1936	Nov. 1962	924,151
349	32349	Dec. 1920	Aug. 1939	Nov. 1962	
350	32350	Dec. 1920	Nov. 1936	Nov. 1962	
351	32351	Jan. 1921	May. 1936	Nov. 1962	
352	32352	Feb. 1921	Sep. 1937	Nov. 1962	
353	32353	Mar. 1921	Jul. 1937	Dec. 1962	867,911

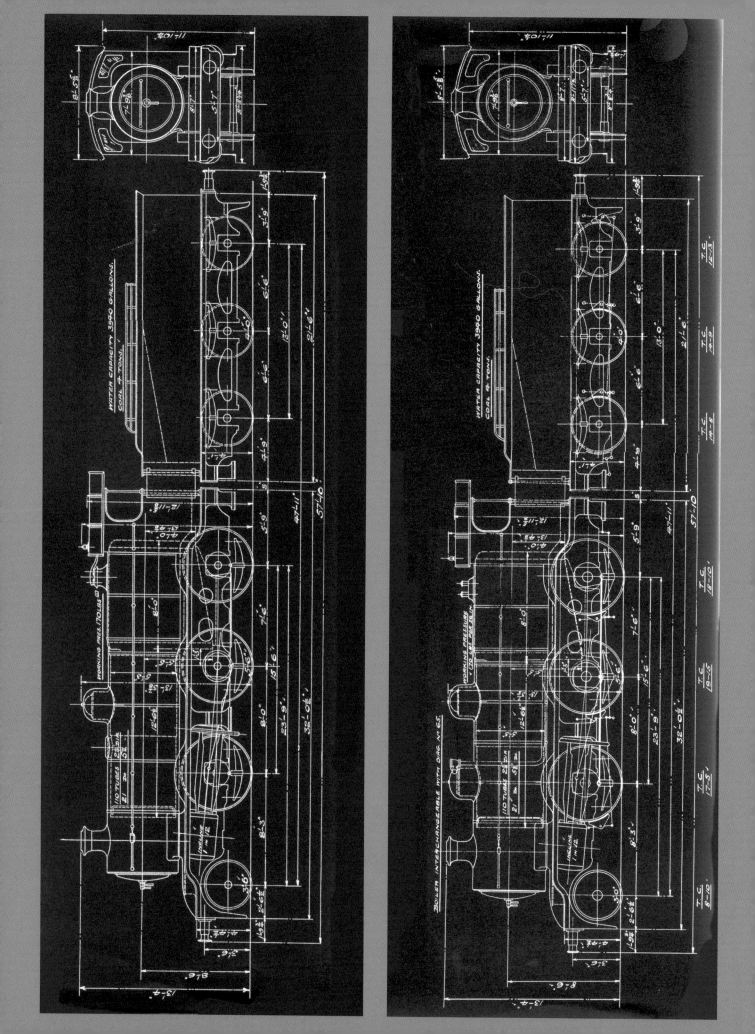

the backdrop of a backlog of work already existing meant the Brighton boiler shop could not commit to manufacture. Enquiries from most outside suppliers revealed the same story with just one organisation, the only positive response coming from the Midland Railway at derby who agreed to supply by August 1920.

The first of the new boilers arrived in March 1920 but perhaps as an indication of the pressure then prevailing at Brighton, it was instead used on No. 237 at the time in the works and awaiting a new firebox. After this matters did proceed apace and the next seven new boilers were indeed fitted to new construction, the engines taking the numbers 347 to 353.

For reasons not explained by Bradley, the final three engines of the batch were postponed and when the last two boilers were delivered, as late as March 1921, they were instead allocated to a pair of B4X 4-4-0 type.

The question of completing the order was raised again in late 1922 but in view of the impending grouping no action was taken. The issue of completing the order neatly passed to the new owners, the Southern Railway. Interestingly the accountants figures show that £844 had already been allocated against the three, consisting of monies spent on bought in parts, including wheels, axles, types, cylinders and Weir pumps; does this indicate that these same components had been purchased from outside for the earlier engines?

The business of leaving the new owners to 'pick up the pieces' so to speak was not without precedent. Several of the pre-group companies adopted similar tactics on the basis of why spend further of the shareholders monies when there will no consequential return. Digressing very slightly, perhaps one of the worst (?) examples was the Taff Vale Railway where almost as soon as grouping was confirmed, major repairs on locomotives ceased so that by 31 December 1922 literally lines of locomotives stood unserviceable and awaiting repairs; a problem neatly passed to the new owners, in this case the GWR.

To return to what was now the Southern Railway, the remaining three engines from the order were never built.

The rational for this decision came from two events. The first in early 1924 when comparative trails were held on trains of 65 wagons between Woking and Eastleigh. The classes selected were the S15, N, N1, and K. The K was not impressive, the S15 without

Cab view of an unknown new engine. Controls are rudimentary yet functional. Left-hand drive although the regulator - shown here fully open - may be operated from either side; useful when shunting. Note the gauges are all attached to the cab side sheets. Screw reverser and just one seat for the crew; on the fireman's side.

doubt the best performer with the two-cylinder N a fairly close second. The N1 was the most economical on coal but its calculated average repair costs were 47% higher than the N. Add to this that the SR were offered 50 engines of the type from Woolwich Arsenal at below cost and the needs of the Southern for a capable mixed traffic engine were thus sated and there was thus no need for the additional K's.

Even so the K class continued to appreciate on what was now the classed as the Central section of the SR; assisted no doubt by a case of old company loyalty.

As might be expected various modifications were also made over the years. Excluding the top feed and second dome previously referred to, these included: No. 340, fitted with a Worthington-Simpson pump and feed water heater in place of the Weir pump and standard condensing system. This was from May 1922 to December 1923 but was noted to increase coal consumption slightly.

Nos 341 and 342 were fitted with Kyala variable blastpipe between March 1922 and April 1923. On

Opposite - K class locos in original and with modified boiler; the latter incorporating the top feed within the second dome.

Likely taken just before or soon after Southern Railway takeover, this unknown example of the class is in charge of a race special running under the gantry's of the 'elevated electric'. To note is that the Weir feed pump was positioned on the left hand side of the framing (looking forward) and the Westinghouse air pump on the right.

this occasion the results were mixed despite the same crews, runs and grades of coal being used.

No 341, February 1923 equipped with Lamberts wet sanding gear to all coupled wheels. Results were good except it tended to fail in very cold weather. Over time additional wear was noted on the wheels of the driven axle. The gear was removed and standard dry sanding substituted in January 1931.

No 351 squired a lengthened smokebox in April 1921 to accommodate a Lewis Draft Appliance. In consequence an external elliptical chimney was also fitted. Various modifications were made from this time on to January 1927 which included the refitting of a standard chimney - which incidentally did improve steaming - but the results obtained whilst indicating a slight improvement in coal consumption were probably insufficient to warrant the initial costs and maintenance. According to Bradley the extended smokebox improved the appearance of the class.

No 352. In February 1923 the existing Weir pump was replaced by a similar device manufactured by Messrs G D Peters. After trails it was established maintenance was more costly than the original equipment; the latter refitted in November 1924.

Up to 1923 black was the standard livery for the class after which matters became somewhat convoluted at which stage we must once again turn to Bradley.

It might be expected that subsequent to this date Southern green might be applied but instead Nos 337, 342 and 344 were instead presented in umber with accompanying Brighton style lettering (SR or LBSCR?)

and numbers. The reversion to passenger livery perhaps a reflection on the fact the class were to be seen on certain passenger workings.

Later the same year we may reasonable comment that 'instructions had been received' and Nos 345 and 349 appeared in lined black.

A standard was set the following year when passenger green was applied, the first engine to receive this being No 338 in June 1924. During the changeover period there were also instances of Southern number plates on the cabside, Southern tender numerals on the tender - below the previous owner's LBSC identification - and Brighton style numerals on the bufferbeams.

Further modifications saw all the class now equipped for steam heating, the tail rods removed from the pistons and vacuum ejectors fitter. At some point the tender coal rails were also plated.

Notwithstanding the decision not to extend the number of engines two new boilers were constructed at Brighton although it will be recalled these were also interchangeable with those fitted to the B4X 4-4-0 class of engines.

Visibly the greatest change to the engines was a reduction in height from the previous generous LBSCR loading gauge to suit the composite gauge applicable to the Eastern and Western sections. This in itself begs the question how were the earlier trials between Woking and Eastleigh carried out?

No 338 was the first to be partially treated at Eastleigh in November 1929 where it had been allocated fro

Above - No 344 of December 1916, likely brand new at Brighton running shed. Separate top feed and livery likely in lined black.

Bottom - No 348, new in December 1920 and fitted with double dome boiler, that at the front housing the top-feed.

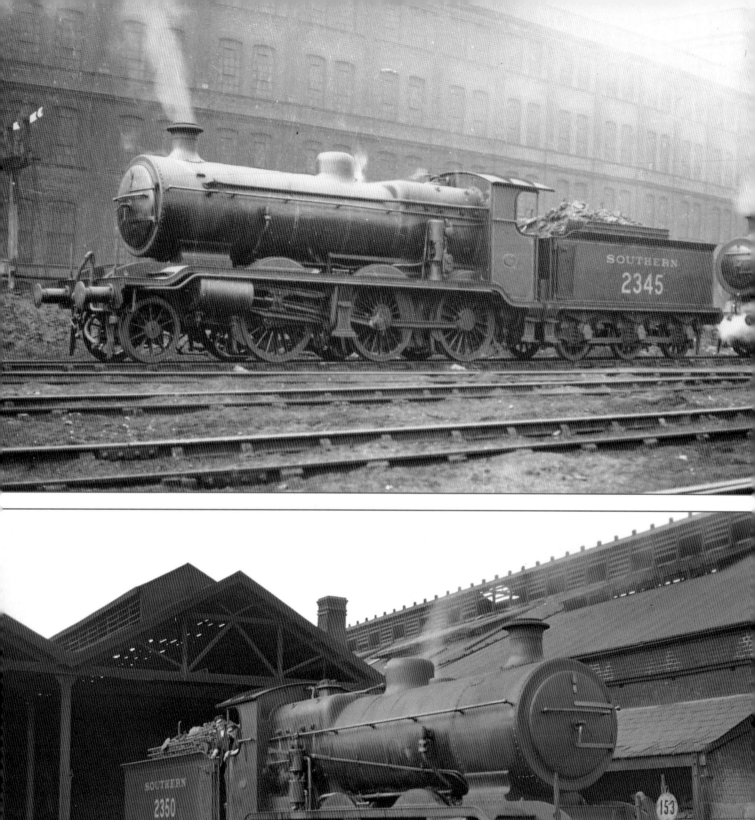

Opposite top - Against the unmistakable backdrop of the storage repository at Stewarts Lane, No 2345 stands awaiting its next duty. Boiler feed is now via clack boxes on the side, cab, dome and chimney also cut down. Plating added to the tender coal rails.

Opposite bottom - Seen from the opposite side, No 2350 displays similar modifications. Dare the say the chimney has a distinct similarity to a Swindon product.

Above - Ex-works at Eastleigh; notice the apprentice dealing with some task by the centre driving wheel. Temporary three link coupling attached.

overhaul. No 343 similarly modified six months later. The work involved reducing the height of the rail to cab height from the previous 13' 4⅛" to 12' 8⅞" which was achieved with the provision of a cab roof having a similar profile to that of the Ashford moguls. At the same time the whistle was re-sited from the previous position proud of the cab roof to a new location on the safety valve casing.

With hindsight the logic to these changes are slightly difficult to understand as at the time no alterations were made to the height of the chimney or dome as both of these still remained proud of the 13' level. Indeed it was not until July 1935 when the now renumbered 2341 left Eastleigh with both these items similarly reduced in height, the details as follows:

Rail level to top of Dome:13' 3⅞" to 12' 7½
Rail level to top of Chimney: 13/42 to 12' 11⅞"

All the class had been likewise dealt with by August 1939, the last being No 2349.

Further changes were the abandoning of top feed and a reversion to clacks mounted on the boiler side, With one exception, on boiler No 1047, Ross-pop safety valves in place of the Ramsbottom type and a less than obvious change which was when the existing Robinson superheater was substituted for a Maunsell type.

Later changes involved substituting standard hot-water injector for Weir pump which task was completed in 1952. Unlike the Ashford design Moguls of the N, N1,

U, and U1 classes, smoke deflectors were never fitted. Aside from the addition of 2000 to the individual class numbers, it was not until the tenure of Mr Bulleid that further external livery changes took place.

The first was in June 1939 when the tender of No 2347 was presented in olive green but paired with the engine in Maunsell green. A misunderstanding had resulted in that it was the tender from No 2037 *Selsey Bill* which should have received the new livery. The tender from No 2037 was quickly repainted in the correct shade.

It was December 1939 before No 2346 left works in unlined dark green and Bulleid lettering. A similar style was applied to Nos 2348, 2351 and 2353 up to March 1941 although not before Nos 2337 and 2350 had received Malachite in November 1940. Thereafter all repaints were in plain black. Bradley comments that the work at Eastleigh in November 1940 and the quality of the paint used was such that No 2337 carried its green livery beyond nationalisation in 1948.

Although originally intended for use on the Brighton (Central) section, the class did stray far and wide especially in the period 1939-45.

As such they were recorded at Ashford, Tonbridge, Southampton, Salisbury and Bournemouth, No 2346 venturing as far as Weymouth in December 1942. Early the following year the four of the class based at New Cross were transferred to Feltham. Their place taken by a similar number of the class from Norwood and which were in turn replaced by N class 2-6-0s. Again we now witness the affection in which the K's were held as the Norwood replacements were regarded with disgust. The Feltham allocation lasted only during wartime and post-war the allocation returned to former Brighton line sheds with the greatest number concentrated at Brighton itself.

Between December 1947 and January 1951, No 2342 was fitted with electric lighting.

Repainting in lined black was first applied to No 32339 at Brighton in January 1949, whilst sister engine No 2343 ran for a short time with the temporary 's' prefix.

July 1950 saw several of the class involved in running trains from Waterloo to Farnborough for the Farnborough air-show. Owing to a shortage of passenger stock on the region, air-braked sets of former Great Eastern passenger stock was borrowed and for which the K class were ideal. Six of the class were intended to be involved, Nos 32337, 32339, 32342, 32345, 32348 and 32349. Of these, No 32337 was found to be unfit upon arrival at Feltham - perhaps meaning all were allocated to Feltham for the duration - whilst No 32349 never in fact left the Central section. These duties were shared with four similarly equipped ex SECR locos.

The class were also involved in a number of accidents and derailments over the years, although in reality no more than might be expected with any group of similar engines. Bradley reports the first in April 1918 when No 340 parted its train in Redhill tunnel and which was subsequently run into by an explosives special and an up goods. Fortunately there was no explosion and the line was cleared in 40 hours. Other events included No 32341 falling into the turntable pit at Brighton on 23 April 1953 and just five days later sister No 32339 running away at Littlehampton and coming to rest just feet from a group of residential dwellings.

More spectacular and no doubt just as terrifying was when No 32346 ran out of control on 3 March 1954 with an 800 ton engineer's train and was eventually brought to rest at catch points at the Groombridge end of Forest Row station. Equally dramatic had been the running away of No 32347 from Bricklayers Arms to Rotherhithe Road on 14 October 1951 where the engine collided with and destroyed the tender of L No 31741, The K was repaired and returned to traffic.

Notwithstanding their origins at Brighton, in the 1930s Eastleigh had responsibility for all repairs. This lasted until WW2 when first Brighton and then later Ashford became involved.

The intention had been for Eastleigh to again assume responsibility later but by February 1954 Ashford had assumed responsibility for all 17 engines simply because Eastleigh was at capacity. The solidly built design served the well over the years and unlike the Ashford moguls no expensive frame repairs were even needed on the class. As such the decision to withdraw the class at the end of 1962 was even more strange with the Ashford locos often needing frame repairs and new cylinders costing in excess of £6K at this same time.

Opposite, 'home and away'. Top: No 32352 near Hailsham with a local service of three modern Mk 1 coaches; the fireman clearly glad to be recorded.

Bottom - No 32353 by North Pole Junction signal box (West London extension line), Saturday 8 August 1959. The engine is almost certainly involved in through train working between the Southern and Midland / Eastern regions.

Above - Wayside shunting for No 32340, location unknown and clearly fresh from overhaul.

Opposite top - The headcode disc is somewhat superfluous here as No 32351 is temporarily missing its centre driving wheels. Ashford works, 12 September 1954. Note too the front lamp brackets have been reduced in height from the original. Following repair, the position of the cabside numeral transfers could vary slightly between works.

Opposite bottom - Just 18 moths before withdrawal, No 32344 is seen in the erecting shop at Eastleigh, 30 April 1961.

Railtour duty for the class was limited, although No 32353 was used by the Sussex branch of the RCTS on 7 October 1962 for their 'Sussex Special' railtour. The K used for the return leg from Brighton to London Bridge running via the usual less than direct Hove, Shoreham, Steyning, Horsham, Dorking North, Leatherhead, Epson, Sutton, Mitcham Junction, Streatham , Tulse Hill and Peckham Rye route.

After storage in the goods yard at Hove, three Nos 32337, 32340 and 32343 made their way north and east to Norwich for scrap. One, No 32347 was broken up outside the shed at Stewarts Lane and the rest met their end at Eastleigh. None would survive into preservation and although one had been earmarked by the Bluebell, the priority at the time had been to purchase the line itself and the opportunity was lost.

A C Perryman in his book 'Life at Brighton Loco. Works' Oakwood Press 1971, recounts how on one occasion a K was being forcibly removed from the workshop before all the brake gear had been refitted; apparently there had been a rush job and the fitters had been told to complete the task outside. Unfortunately it was a definite case of more haste and less speed, as the brake gear slipped and fell digging into the floor just as the engine was part way out of the doors. The engine could not be moved forward or back and there she remained until after the bank holiday when the relevant items were cut off with a torch and there was a fortnight's delay before new items could be made by the smith.

Harold Holcroft afford a professional dissertation in 'Locomotive Adventure Vol 2'. Ian Allan 1965. In this he refers to a run with No 2352 hauling a 956 ton train from Norwood Junction to Three Bridges on 11 October 1936, with the test made for the purpose of obtaining data for the Electrical Engineer as to the design of a future electric locomotive. Holcroft commented that at one point the train was deliberately stopped at which point it was noted the brake blocks on the engine

Opposite top - On shed at Eastleigh. The class worked regular freight services on the coast line from Brighton often stopping at Chichester to reform the train. Chichester yard was for decades an important goods facility working seven days a week. As if to indicate the downturn in traffic that occurred in the early 1960s, the yard was closed on Sundays from the end of 1962. The engines would also work the regular stock trains between lancing and Eastleigh.

Opposite bottom - No 32345 K in the shadow of Reading East Main signal box.

This page, top - 'All mod cons'; ATC battery box on No 32343.

This page, bottom - Unusual location and working. No 32345 is coming off the West of England line at Worting Junction heading for Basingstoke and London. Most likely the engine was attached at Salisbury.

and tender were red hot. At this point the associated section of type was similarly being heated and which cased the friction to diminish meaning the train would move forward a few inches accompanied by assorted groans until a cooler section of tyre was reached. Not relevant to the K class but of related interest is that Holcroft added shortly after a trial with a lesser weight train and an electric motor coach as the power (having both motor bogies powered) was carried out.

Holcroft considered the K lacked the versatility of the Ashford moguls on fast passenger work. This on account of the inclined cylinders, large heavy pistons and lower boiler pressure; 170psi, subsequently increased to 180psi, against 200psi. Even so they were often seen on similar duties to the Ashford types.

As they fell by the wayside it was stated by offialdom that the class to be sent to Stewarts Lane for storage. This however was not the case and instead they congregated in the goods yard at Hove; some even arriving in steam having been at work just a few hours earlier.

Having quickly establish there would be no salvation most ended their days at Eastleigh, although three were sold for scrap at Norwich and one cut up outside the shed at Stewarts Lane. Their replacements were N class engines themselves redundant from the West Country.

References are as mentioned in the text and also D L Bradley's, *Locomotives of the LBSCR. Part 3*, published by the RCTS. 1974.

The last engines.......

Above - A wasted resource (as of course was the end for so many other engines at this time many with a good few years of useful life left), No 32351 awaits the inevitable at Eastleigh, 3 March 1963. The location is the scrap / works line running around the south side of Eastleigh shed. Passing by the on the main line it was possible to glimpse some of what was present, that is until the view was obstructed by the partial embankment of what had once been intended to be the flyover for the Fareham line - never built. In the open this and others would deteriorate, one, No 32353 was still intact - minus rods of course - at Eastleigh on 9 November 1963 and consequently may well have been the very last to remain intact. *Tony Molyneaux*

Opposite top - No 32337 awaiting its fate at King's scrapyard in Norwich. This engine does not appear to have been fitted with AWS and it will be noted the smokebox door handles have been removed meaning the door had to be prevented from opening with rope. This was one of three if the class to meet its end here.

Opposite bottom - The remains of what had once been No 32347 outside Stewarts Lane shed. As to why this one engine met its end here is lost in the midst of time. Certain scrap merchants did indeed cut up engines 'on site' so to speak but this was usually when the culprit was not deemed fit to travel. None of the class were ever named.

Next time: The N15X type, 'Remembrance' class 4-6-0s

Now a slightly unlikely request perhaps: on page 68 in particular we give a short biography on Arthur Earle Edwards. Occasional photographs by this SR and BR(S) employee are known to have appeared in publications especially in the 1940s and 1950s. Does anyone by chance have any idea where his collection may be lodged - or even if it survived?

Down the line to Oxted: Part 1
Alan Postlethwaite

The Oxted line was a last outpost of steam from London into East Surrey and beyond. Let us take a ride to enjoy the glorious North Downs scenery. We can catch a train throughout the day from the Brighton side of Victoria or during the rush hour from London Bridge low-level.

All photos are copyright of the Bluebell Railway Photographic Archives.

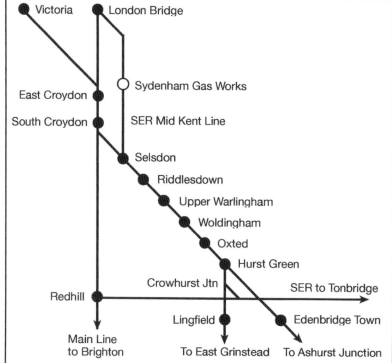

Just south of New Cross Gate, LMS class 4P tank No. 42103 heads a train of birdcage stock from London Bridge to Tunbridge Wells West. In the days of BR steam, Oxted trains from London ran to Tunbridge Wells West via East Grinstead or terminated at East Grinstead or Forest Row. A few ran half to Eastbourne and half to Brighton, swapping halves at Eridge with a second train from Tonbridge. The railway went to extraordinary trouble for the convenience of the few passengers who travelled the full distance. *John J Smith, 1959*

At Clapham Junction, a class 4MT tank restarts a train from Tunbridge Wells to Victoria. One of the last locomotives to be built at Brighton, No. 80151 is preserved on the Bluebell Railway. *Alan Postlethwaite, 1961*

In Clapham cutting we see the rear of an Up Oxted train. On the right wall are remnants of brackets of the LBSCR overhead electric system. The siding on the left leads to the LSWR milk platform. The junction, far right beyond the bridge, serves the West London line. *Alan Postlethwaite, 1961*

The main line between East Croydon and Redhill was jointly owned by the SER and LBSCR. The SER built two branches off the main line, respectively to Tattenham Corner and Caterham. The latter runs in parallel with the Oxted line for several miles, within a stone's throw in places.

Between East Croydon and South Croydon, the left-hand arch of this gantry covered the Oxted line which was single and reversible on this short stretch. Down Oxted trains could alternatively use the Brighton Down Local, hence the Distant arm on post 3. The miniature repeaters at ground level are a delight, worthy of a Hornby O gauge layout. *John J Smith collection, 1900-1930.*

Note the top of main post is missing on the original scan.

It was always a thrill to alight from a 4-SUB unit at East Croydon to await the train to Oxted. Then came the anomaly of two Oxted trains passing on the wrong side. Here, LMS class 4P tank No. 42090 arrives at platform 5 with a Down train while an Up service departs platform 6, about to tackle the intricacies of the Croydon Tangle. *Alan Postlethwaite, 1959*

A departing train can evoke wistful feelings. If we had caught this one, might we have spent the afternoon exploring Tunbridge Wells? This is Selsdon. The rear coach is SECR 'Continental Stock' of 1921 vintage. The train is nicely framed by semaphore arms, the signal box and a fogman's hut. Coming in from the left, the SER's mid-Kent link opened in 1884 and was severed in 1983. *Alan Postlethwaite, 1958*

At Selsdon, class E4X tank No. 32466 heads an East Croydon train of birdcage stock to Tonbridge. *Colin Hogg, 1954*

Class BB No. 34089 *602 Squadron* charges along the disused Down platform at Selsdon. The platforms on the Brighton side closed in 1917 as a wartime economy measure and never reopened. This a troop train from Victoria via the Crowhurst loop. Destination Shornecliffe, perhaps? *Colin Hogg, 1953*

Above: The Oxted line was electrified in 1935 from Selsdon to Sanderstead and was fully electrified in 1987. On a chilly spring morning on the Surrey hills, class 4MT No. 80068 emerges from Riddlesdown tunnel whose signal box was disused. It is interesting that none of the photographers herein bothered with the intermediate stations. We were too absorbed trying to capture the last decade of steam in this intriguing chalk landscape.
Alan Postlethwaite, 1961

Right: The Croydon, Oxted & East Grinstead Railway opened in 1884. It was joint SER/ LBSCR as far as the Crowhurst spur and pure LBSCR beyond . The line was difficult to build with three long tunnels and the tall Warlingham viaduct, seen here with class 4MT tank No. 80139.
Alan Postlethwaite, 1961

Departing Upper Warlingham, class H2 No. 32425 *Trevose Head* heads a set of SECR stock to the south coast, possibly Eastbourne. Many Brighton locomotives survived into the Late Steam Age but very little Brighton coaching stock did likewise other than conversions to push-pull or EMU. *John J Smith, 1954*

Opposite, top: Up-sun silhouettes can be dramatic. Here, class W tank No. 31919 approaches Woldingham with a banana train from Avonmouth to Lingfield where there was a ripening shed. The pick-up goods service from Norwood Junction also terminated at Lingfield. Irregular services included horse boxes and race day specials to Lingfield and hop-picker specials between London Bridge low-level and Hawkhurst. Coal from Erith North Quay to Sydenham gas works could be routed via Maidstone West, Tonbridge, the Crowhurst spur and Selsdon. At night, however, Sydenham coal trains would take a much shorter route by reversing at St Johns, Brockley Lane or Bricklayers Arms. *Alan Postlethwaite, 1961*

Opposite, bottom: Class 4MT tank No. 80143 approaches the south portal of Oxted tunnel, a mile long through the North Downs. Components of concrete cable ducts are laid out as part of power signalling work in progress. *Alan Postlethwaite, 1961*

Part 2 will appear in Issue 7

An alternative to preservation
BR's plans to electrify all or part of the Bluebell Railway
Plus some notes on Arthur Earle Edwards

As at my previous journal, I remain ever grateful to a number of individuals who regularly send me originals or copies of documents likely saved from the skip and which when looked at today reveal a fascinating insight into the mindset of the Southern Railway and / or Southern Region decades past.

One recent example was track-spreading with Leader – see ST4 - and we are now delighted to present another example from history this time a consideration to electrify all or part of the Bluebell line from East Grinstead through to Horsted Keynes or possibly even down as far as Culver Junction and on to Lewes.

From the available information it must be pointed out that what is present is certainly just a small part of a correspondence file, the personal papers of Arthur Earle Edwards, who at the time of his retirement in the 1960s held the position of Chief Operating Superintendent of the Southern Region. If the memory of the present writer is correct, Mr Earle Edwards also had a regular Friday evening (?) BBC radio slot in the 1960s where he would describe potential weekend engineering works and possible traffic disruption that might in consequence occur on the Southern Region. (If any reader can provide more on this aspect alone we would be grateful – Ed.) The papers referred to below date from 1956/1957 and are cross-referenced to various other correspondence from around that time but which, regretfully, is not present.

At this stage we should briefly recount the history of the Bluebell line, more accurately the Lewes and East Grinstead Railway which had originally opened in 1882

The 7.58am Lewes to East Grinstead departing West Hoathly, No year is given but we may state it is prior to 1956. August 1956.
Gerald Daniels

between East Grinstead and Culver Junction north of Lewes. The following year 1883, Horsted Keynes became a junction with a connection to a 4½ mile line west through Ardingly to Copyhold Junction north of Haywards Heath on the main London to Brighton line. The route from East Grinstead to Horsted Keynes and thence via Ardingly back on to the main line was also an occasional useful diversionary route. The Southern Railway electrified the Ardingly line to Horsted Keynes in 1932 with the new electric service seeing 18 trains a day half of which terminated as a shuttle service at Haywards Heath although the remainder continued on to Seaford.

North and south of Horsted Keynes diminishing traffic receipts on what was without doubt a rural byway serving only limited areas of population, resulted in

Right: Posted from East Grinstead. The small type includes mention that tickets for journeys commencing at Newick & Chailey, Sheffield Park, and West Hoathley will be issues on the train so implying these stations were now unstaffed.
Gerald Daniels

Bottom: Following the revision of services, this was the first train at Horstead Keynes; the 9.30am from Lewes, due here at 10.04. (We are not told if it ran on time!) 'K' No 32342 is in charge of just two coaches and clearly has steam to spare.
Gerald Daniels

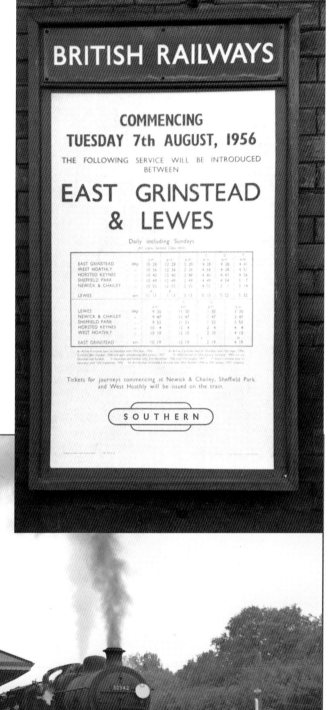

the branch line committee of British Railways viewing the continuation of passenger services between Lewes and East Grinstead as not financially viable. Notwithstanding the expected challenge by local residents, passenger services were withdrawn officially from 15 June 1955 although in practice they ceased two weeks earlier on 29 May on account of the ASLEF strike of the time. Recall this only affected the Lewes to East Grinstead trains, the electric service to Horsted Keynes continuing to operate.

What followed was almost an 'Oh Mr Porter' farce as a local resident, Margery Bessemer (grand-daughter of the famed steel maker Sir Henry Bessemer) and hailing from Chailey – which village was served by Newick & Chailey station south of Horsted Keynes - discovered the original Acts authoring the L & EG railway included a clause insisting on a minimum level of service. The clause in these Acts had never been repealed and in consequence British Railways were compelled to restore a passenger service from 7 August 1956 but with trains only calling at the original three stations mentioned in the Acts, namely Sheffield Bridges (sic), Newick (sic), and West Hoathly. The restoration was of course only temporary and it was inevitable the clauses in the original Acts would be repealed by Parliament resulting in a second, and final closure by British Railways from 17 March 1958. The rest as they say, is history, and we may be grateful to the early pioneers of standard gauge preservation and their modern day counterparts that part at least of the original route remains open.

So where does this leave the crux of this piece? Well simply that in the papers of Mr Earle Edwards there appears a memorandum having the rather long title, 'Stage 2 (Central Section) electrification of main lines with dieselisation of secondary lines and elimination of steam in this area.'

'A Earle Edwards Esq' is written by hand at the top of page 1 and in consequence it is not totally clear if this was a memorandum produced by him or he was instead simply a recipient; we suspect the latter. There is also no confirmed date although there is mention of an 'Electrification Committee Minute No 152 of 15 June 1956. Noticeably absent from the front page is the usual long list of persons making up the normal committee / distribution.

What the reader should bear in mind with what follows is that this document is clearly running 'parallel' with the Southern Region's own wish to close the Bluebell line and in consequence we may ask was it a simple 'left hand – right hand' situation?

We need not consider irrelevant parts of the report which relate to other lines but of particular interest is the heading 'Standard Interval Service (off Peak)', where in tabular form the actual train services are mentioned.

To ensure there is no confusion the headings in the following table are identical to that shown together with the associated footnote.

Standard Service	Electric or Diesel	Basic Unit	Trains per hour	Divide at
Victoria Seaford * front portion, Tunbridge Wells West rear portion.	Electric	2 x 2 Hap	1	Hurst Green

* Via East Grinstead taking up existing Hosted Keynes – Seaford service.

Left: To perhaps muted celebration, the 'first train' (after the reinstatement that is, at Newick & Chailey.

Top: Reported as the 1.30pm Lewes to East Grinstead, which according to the timetable would depart at 2.04pm.

Right: The 12.25pm East Grinstead to Lewes leaving Newick & Chailey. Again the engine is C2X No 32442. Four trains operated each way, timed so that a single locomotive and crew were all that was required for the passenger service.

Images Gerald Daniels

We then move on to the star item. A further note comments on previous letters dated 18 January and 5 April 1957 (unfortunately not in the file), but continues, 'Line East Grinstead to Horsted Keynes to be electrified to provide direct link from Oxted to the Coast'. The paperwork then refers to another (missing) letter of 17 April 1957 but against which is typed 'Consider re-opening Kingscote and West Hoathley stations'.

Under the heading 'Action taken' both the points about electrification and the station re-openings were marked as 'Incorporated in plan', whilst in addition a handwritten 'yes' (perhaps by AEE himself) is marked against both. Associated with this was 'East Grinstead – Low Level Station to be re-opened with signalling improvements. Electrified sidings required'.

At this point our story ends – well almost - as the slim file includes also contains a schematic drawing of the proposed routes to be electrified; the surprise this time being that from East Grinstead south the whole of the Bluebell line appears to be the subject of an electrification proposal. Whether this was drawn in error is not mentioned but there can be no doubt over its intention. Unfortunately nothing further is mentioned in the paperwork.

Few definite conclusions may be drawn, for without the remainder of the file and associated paperwork it is impossible to be certain of what transpired in the interim. Factually of course we know the line was closed, electrification never did take place and of course Horsted Keynes lost its electric service when the Ardingly line was closed in late October 1963. Perhaps the most obvious thoughts are that the Southern Region drew up plans for what was the ideal scenario but then restriction on capital expenditure prevented these proposals from going ahead.

In his book 'An Illustrated History of the Lewes & East Grinstead Railway', (OPC-2000), author Klaus Marx refers to earlier Southern Railway plans for electrification between Horsted Keynes and East Grinstead in 1935, and states, '…despite the lobbying by residents of Oxted, East Grinstead and elsewhere…..only the outbreak of war in 1939 prevented plans for electrification going further north' (– by this he is referring to north of Horsted Keynes). At this point we should state that in the 1956/57 paperwork which forms the principal of this piece there are no references back to earlier plans. Marx later refers to anticipated residential development in the area around East Grinstead as justification for the BR revival of the electrification scheme but then

'A hollow victory'. The platform at East Grinstead thronged for what would genuinely be the last day of working under BR; 16 March 1958 - and not a single third-rail 'pot' in sight! The preservation society was formed almost a exactly one year later on 15 March 1959 and re-opening to East Grinstead finally took place on 23 March 2013. *Gerald Daniels*

counters this with comment on potential Green Belt restrictions which would conversely affect traffic growth.

The last word is left to the final page of the report which refers to an implementation date for 'Stage 2, 750v dc third rail Central section' as June 1959.

On the next line is written 'Stage 3 25 Kv / 6.6 Kv 50 cycle Overhead, Western Section': June 1962.
Accordingly we have to leave the proposal(s) in limbo. Did Southern Region managers really not communicate to such an extend that one half were intent on closure and the other on electrification, for that is certainly the impression we get here. In the end it was a pared down electrification scheme that was approved, the funds simply not available to support electrification everywhere. Sir Brian Robertson, then Chairman of the BTC indicated as such when the Bluebell was

temporarily re-opened in 1956 simply stating that the running costs for the restored service would have to be found through savings elsewhere. Available finance was also the reason another contemporary proposal, that of electrifying the line from Brighton to Horsham via Steyning was shelved. Nowadays we may refer to the 'spark' effect; meaning electrification and with a faster service encouraging patronage, but then the Southern Railway had already discovered this pre WW2. It needed investment in the 1950s for electrification to work and what money was available from government for modernisation was of necessity split between all the regions and in turn prioritised within each.

One day perhaps we may come across what we have no doubt would be an equally fascinating file of papers on Stage 3.

Right: The final Up train in the platforms at East Grinstead.

Bottom: The final Bluebell line train shunting at East Grinstead.

Both Gerald Daniels

Arthur Earle Edwards.

Mention has been made of the above individual in this article and in consequence it may be appropriate to describe more of the man.

Arthur Edwards was born on 29 May 1901, the third child and eldest son of Arthur Thomas Bachelor Edwards and Louisa Ellen Edwards in Maidstone. His father and paternal grandfathers were both railway signalmen: ATB was born in Charlton but his father was born in Horsham, Sussex.

He started his railway career in 1917 with the SECR and was attached to the Superintendent of the Line Office (Military) dealing with ambulance train traffic. As a young man he clearly came to the attention of others as he soon moved to become the personal clerk to the Chief of the Passenger Train section. With the grouping in 1923 and formation of the Southern Railway, his role was first in the Special Traffic Section and then in the Train Running Section of the East London Divisional Superintendents' Office.

In 1923 he was rewarded (?) by the General Manager for promptitude in averting an accident (?) to a London – Hastings express. This was followed by further congratulations in January 1927 reference a number of suggestions made.

In the same year1927, he was selected for what we would now regard as management training. At the time such young men so chosen were referred to as Cadets. During the course of his training he also visited railway installations in a number of European countries.

In 1931 he was in post as the Assistant Superintendent at Exeter and it was noted by now also held several academic qualifications as well as being an associate member of at least one professional institute. He remained at Exeter though the 1930s being appointed Senior Assistant from 1 May 1934. His was clearly a high profile role as there are frequent newspaper reports of Southern Railway happenings in the South West where his name occurs.

He married Clarice Mabel Howe in the Exeter Registration District in 1938 and in 1939 was noted as resident at the Polygon Hotel in Southampton; almost certainly a billet for WW2 work in the Southampton area.

Assuming he remained at Southampton post 1939, in 1944-1945 he was Acting Assistant (Planning) at Headquarters in the General Manager's office.

Two years later he was recorded as Assistant to the Divisional Superintendent London (West) at Woking. Under BR we have him as District Traffic Superintendent Orpington in Commercial and Operating Department covering the period 1951-1957 and which therefore makes it slightly strange how he became involved with electrification plans that was clearly out of his area.

Whatever, another move is report for 1959-1960 when he was Operating Officer in Traffic Organisation before a final mention as Movement Officer in the General Manager's Department in 1962-1963.

Arthur Earle Edwards latterly made his home in Marlings Park Avenue, Chislehurst being referred to by his staff (behind his back) as 'The Earl'. He died in Farnborough hospital on 11 August 1965. His widow survived until January 1971 and was by then living at Taunton.

Obviously the Lewisham, St Johns accident happened on his patch but there is no mention of him in the Inspector's Report.

With thanks to: John Creed, Tony Hillman, Gerry Nichols, Roger Merry-Price.

References; 'The Railway Year Book' – various issues.

An Illustrated History of the Lewes & East Grinstead Railway, (OPC-2000)

W34 *Newport* leaving Ryde St Johns sometime in 1952. W34 is on a Ventnor train and passing the loco and carriage works on the right - the locomotive shed was on the left. In the opinion of many, this particular shade of Southern green allied to 'Sunshine' lettering suited the class well, similarly the red coaching stock. The train length would appear to be at least six vehicles a fair pull for a little engine especially as the stock is likely to be well filled in what was late spring / early summer time; the engine sanding is being used.

SCT made at least three visits to the island, in 1951, 1952 and 1957. His area of professional responsibility appears to have extended to the island lines although was it coincidence he just happened to be present for the RCTS tour depicted overleaf - probably not!

On his final visit taking colour of the island lines, he seems to have recorded just three views, including this one, right, of St Lawrence tunnel on the Ventnor West line, now devoid of track. Perhaps he was even recalling his visit to the station for the special in May 1952.. . .see page 71.

Don't forget, copies of the S C Townroe colour images are available as downloads for public or commercial use. Please contact the editor for details.

On 18 May 1952 SCT was on hand to record W3 in the process of running round at Cowes with the RCTS South of England branch, 'Isle of Wight Railtour'.

This really was a wonderful opportunity for a day out although it is curious to note there was one section of line not traversed; that from Sandown south through Shanklin and Wroxall to Ventnor (Town). We can find no reason for this so the obvious conclusion must be simply the time available.

The participants would have congregated at Portsmouth to take the ferry to Ryde where they joined their special train with, we think, W32 *Bonchurch* at the head. This first part of the tour took the special to Newport where we do know No W3 *Ryde* took charge for the short run to Cowes. Our photograph is one of two similar views taken by SCT at Cowes, this image showing the engine running round - the second (not included) has the train ready to leave.

No W3 was only used for the return journey to Newport where it was replaced by W32 again for a trip to Freshwater - run round - and return to Newport. Readers will be aware of a further shunt / run round - manoeuvre that would have been needed again in order that W32 might now head on to the Merstone line to end up at Ventnor West where SCT again took a colour view - *opposite top*.

From Ventnor it was back to the junction at Merstone where No 32 is depicted running around - *opposite bottom*. It is at this point that matters become slightly confused as the Six Bells Junction webside shows that after returning from Ventnor West the train returned to Newport before retracing its steps again to return over the same route to Sandown. This appears to be contradicted by the image opposite, the only practical reason for such a move being line occupancy, but then why would No 32 be running around its train?

Whatever, at Sandown there was another reversal W32 now heading north to Brading and a diversion on to the Bembridge branch. A further run round at the terminus here , back to Brading - run round - and the third engine of the day, W14 *Fishbourne* for the final leg back to Ryde Pier Head.

The participants on the day were almost certainly the last railtour travellers to visit Ventnor West which closed just two months later in July 1952. The following year the branch to Bembridge closed along with the line from Newport westwards to Freshwater. The Newport to Sandown line via Merstone similarly succumbed in 1956.

Having sited Ventnor West and run round there, the train returned to Merstone where No 32 is running around its train. The green livery for No 32 may be noted. The Ventnor West branch diverges to the right; the line to Sandown to the left. Trains from Sandown might use either side of the centre island platform here in order to form a connection with the Ventnor West service if required.

W14 taking water amongst the greenery at Brading on 16 May 1962.

Opposite top: W15 *Cowes* entering Brading with a Ventnor train on 18 May 1952. The observers on the platform are very likely participants from the tour. W15 was one of three of the class withdrawn in the 1950s and in consequence is rare to find in colour.

This page top: The special setting off from Brading bound for Bembridge behind No W14 *Fishbourne*. We cannot explain why in the first view in this series showing the RCTS special taken at Cowes, page 70, the consist is of three coaches and yet here only two re seen.

W34 *Newport* leaving Brading on a regular service train to Ryde. This engine was another early casualty taken out of service in August 1955 and this despite having been on the island only since May 1947.

W27 *Merstone* at Newport shed in July 1951. This was one of a pair of engines sent to the island in March 1926. At this time it had already been in service for nearly 36 years but still had a further 30 years ahead and remained working trains until December 1966.

Comings (without the goings). Top we see W4 *Wroxall* at Medina Wharf in May 1957. Arriving on the island in June 1933 aged 55, this was the last of the four E1 locos to remain in service here and was withdrawn in October 1960. Bottom are the final two members of the O2s class, Nos W35 and W36, later named *Freshwater* and *Carisbrooke* respectively. The view was taken at Southampton Docks in April 1949 with the pair shortly to be transported by barge to the island.

The end of Isle of Wight use for No 13 at Eastleigh in May 1949. No 13 had started life with the LB&SCR as their No 667 taking the number W13 in 1932 to accompany its name *Carisbrooke*.

The 'Terriers' had originally been used on the Ventnor West and Freshwater lines, until strengthening allowed the more numerous O2 class engines to be used. Together with sister W8 *Freshwater*, the pair remained employed mainly on the Merstone - Ventnor West pull-push services although with just two engines of the type remaining on the Island it was hardly economic retaining spares and the pair were despatched to Eastleigh as seen - No W8 painted in plain black at this time.

Both engines were stored at the Eastleigh running shed pending scrap but a reprieve saw the enter works to emerge as Nos 32646 (the former No 8) and 32677 (the former No 13).

As No 32677 the engine now shared duties with other engines of the class on the Hayling Island branch although it was noted that it was transferred from Fratton - the home depot for Hayling Island branch engines, to Ashford from 12 May 1953. No 32677 returned to Fratton resuming its former duties from 14 February 1953 and by now also sporting lined black livery which had been applied at Brighton in September 1952.

Although sister No 32646 survived until the Hayling line closed - and was subsequently preserved, now having a permanent home once again with the Isle of Wight steam railway, No 32677 was not so lucky and was withdrawn in September 1959 having, according to official records, having run some 1,301, 612 miles in a 79 year career. The engine was finally disposed at from Eastleigh Works in May 1960.

Next Time: Mr Bulleid's Pacifics.

Answers to the cartoon quiz from page 77, Issue 5).

The four stations you had to guess were; Kingscote, Longfield Halt, Earley, and Blackfriars. (The cartoon comes from the Southern Region Magazine of September 1949. Further cartoons from the same source will appear in future issue.)

In the meanwhile do look at the bottom of page 79 for a different puzzle submitted by Tony Hillman.

Treasures from the Bluebell Railway Museum
Tony Hillman

Without any specific communication between ourselves, Tony's content for this issue fits in well with out own 'Dark Days of 80 Years Ago' piece.

The subject now the **Re-evacuation of school children from Kent and Sussex.**

Following the fall of France, the Railway Executive Committee met on the 17 June 1940 to discuss the re-evacuation of school children from coastal areas in Southeast England. It was decided that some 10,400 school children, who were evacuated last September to places between Ashford and Seaford, would be re-evacuated on Sunday 23 June to Pembroke, Carmarthen and Brecknock (Brecon) in Wales.

On Sunday 23 June, seven trains ran via Reading and seven via Salisbury. A total of 8270 passengers were carried. Trains started from Seaford, Battle, Hythe, Eastbourne, Hastings, Polegate, Ashford, Rye and Bexhill.

Five trains to Salisbury ran via Lewes, Haywards Heath (reverse) and Preston Park. A note states that it was the responsibility of the Haywards Heath Station Master to arrange for the facing points to be clipped for trains towards Preston Park.

Two trains to Salisbury ran via Clapham Junction, East Putney and Wimbledon.

Trains to Reading ran via Redhill and Guildford.

The empty stock returned to either Reading or Salisbury after approximately 12 hours and was dispersed around the Southern.

On Tuesday 25 June a further two trains were run from Sandwich and Sheerness.

Hastings and St Leonards Observer – Saturday 21 October 1944

If Hitler Had Invaded - Secret Plans for Hastings Evacuation.

"Secret plans prepared in complete detail for the compulsory evacuation in three days of the whole of the civilian population still left in Hastings after the first voluntary evacuation scheme, with the exception of about a thousand people required to stay for Home Guard and Civil Defence duties and other essential services, may now be disclosed. The plans have remained in being until quite recently, for it was only at the end of last month that the Regional Commissioner's direction under which they were prepared was cancelled."

The Whole Population plan for East Sussex, including Hastings, shows fifteen electric trains would run on two days and eleven the following two days. These trains would have capacity for 800 people each. Trains would run from Eastbourne, picking up at Hampden Park and from Seaford picking up at Newhaven. All would run up the Brighton Main Line and via the Quarry Line ending their journeys at Purley, East Croydon, Mitcham Junction, Wallington, Epsom or Victoria.

Fourteen steam hauled trains were planned on the same four days, again with capacity for 800 people on each. Ten would run from Hastings or Ore and four from Bexhill West. Destinations being Haslemere, Reigate,

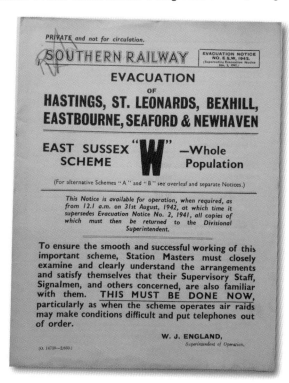

8

SPECIAL LOADED STEAM TRAINS.

Train No.	115	116	117	118a	118b	119	120	121
Provision { Time / From }	Berth. Two 3 C Sts. 3 C Thirds	8†10 a.m. Roberts-bridge.	7†30 a.m. Roberts-bridge.	9†0 a.m. Etchingham.		9†25 a.m. Wadhurst.	10†30 a.m. Wadhurst.	9†15 a.m. Tonbridge.
To convey 1st Day	800	800	Not run. See No. 116	800	Not run.	800	800	800
2nd Day	800	Not run. See No. 117	800	800	Not run.	800	800	800
3rd Day	800	Not run. See No. 117	800	800	Not run.	800	800	800
4th Day	800	Not run. See No. 117	800	Not run.	800	800	400	800

Station	115 arr	115 dep	116 arr	116 dep	117 arr	117 dep	118(1) arr	118(1) dep	118(2) arr	118(2) dep	119 arr	119 dep	120 arr	120 dep	121 arr	121 dep
	A.M.		A.M.		A.M.		A.M.		A.M.		A.M.		A.M.		P.M.	
Ore						9E 2								11E45		
Hastings		8†15		9E 5	9	5						10†20	11	48		12E30
St. Leonards (W.S.)	8†17	8E27									10†22	10E42				
Bo-peep Jc.	8	30	9	10	9	10					10	45	11	54	12	35
West St. Leonards																
Bexhill West								10E 0		10E 0						
Crowhurst	8	36	9	17	9	17	10	10	10	10	10	51	12	0	12	41
Etchingham	8	51	9	37	9	37	10	25	10	25	11	6	12	15	12	56
Tunbridge Wells Ctl.	9	10	10	0	10	0	10	45	10	45	11	26	12	35	1	16
Tonbridge	9	18	10	8	10	8	10 54W	11 0	10	54	11	35	12	45	1	24
Redhill									11	22	11	30				
Reigate																
Dorking Town										11 46						
Shalford Jc.										12 4						
Guildford									12	7	12	15				
Shalford Jc.										12 18						
Haslemere										12D38						
Sevenoaks (T.H.)	9 33W	9 38	10	23	10	23	11	15			11	50	12 59W	1 3	1 39W	1 41
Orpington		9 49T		10 35T		10 35 T		11 27T			12D 2			1 13T		1 53T
Petts Wood Jc.		9 51		10 37		10 37		11 29						1 15		1 55
Chislehurst				10D40		10D40										
Bickley Jc.		9 53L						11 31L						1 17L	1	57L
Bromley South		9 57						11 36						1 22	2D 2	
Beckenham Jc.	10D1	10†11					1140C	1142					1 26C	1 27		
Norwood Jc.							1148 W	1153					1 34W	1 37		
West Croydon								11 59					1 44	1 45		
Waddon Marsh													1 49	1 50		
Beddington Lane													1 54	1 55		
Mitcham Jc.													1 58	1 59		
Mitcham													2 2	2 2½		
Merton Park													2 7	2 7½		
Wimbledon													2D14	2†24		
Tooting														2 30		
Streatham Jc. Sth.														2 33		
Tulse Hill														2 37		
Herne Hill	10	18												2 41		
Brixton	10	20												2 43		
Factory Jc.	10	23												2 46		
Stewarts Lane	10†34												2†55			
Sutton							12	11								
Epsom							12	21								
Leatherhead							12D29	12†39								
Dorking North							12	47								
Horsham							1†11									
Disposal { Time / To }	11†20 a.m. Hastings.		11†10 a.m. Roberts-bridge.		11†10 a.m. Roberts-bridge.		2†10 p.m. Etchinghm.		1†0 p.m. Etchinghm.		12†30 p.m. Wadhurst.		3†25 p.m. Wadhurst.		2†25 p.m. Tonbridge.	

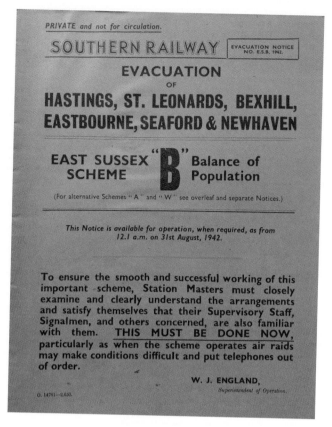

Chislehurst, Beckenham Junction, Wimbledon, Leatherhead and Dorking North.

The 16-page notice includes all the empty stock workings to make up the trains and return after depositing their passengers.

While the Southern Railway organised the trains many other organisations were involved in the operation. Maidstone & District Motor Services would be responsible for getting people to the stations, with lists produced to show who was close enough to walk and who needed transport. The local Council had plans to

move its offices out of the area. Food stores were set up with 48 hours of food available.

Envelopes were produced to be sent out by 'special postal delivery' to each address to inform the public that the evacuation was happening.

The notice for Kent runs to 43 pages and lists 164 trains running over 2 days, again with a capacity of 800 passengers each. For West Sussex there would be 93 electric trains over 4 days, the notice running to 32 pages.

From the *Southern Railway Magazine* November 1930.
Hidden Locomotive Names

'A correspondent submits the following groups of words, each of which, when the letters are re-arranged, will be found to spell the name of a Southern Railway locomotive.'

(Solutions will be given in the next issue).

1. Leeds Main
2. Log Went Nil
3. Ovens Sent
4. Let Bark Bore
5. Sad Vote Here
6. Had Rag Sale
7. London's R A
8. My Golf Arena
9. Mark or Sail
10. Nor Get Bid

Southern Railway Periscope – On Display in the Museum.

When installing or modifying signals the Signalling and Telecommunications Department (S&T) would need to check if the signal was visible to the train crew. Given that when in use the crew would be significantly higher than the S&T staff, they used a periscope which they could raise to the same height as the locomotive crew. They could then check that signals had not been obscured by bridges etc and were visible to the crews. The operator would stand on the ground or platform and raise the top of the periscope to the height of the crew's view and check the signal was visible.

The periscope is of Southern Railway origin and is marked "S&T department, Wimbledon".

In the Museum an '0' gauge signal has been placed on top of a cabinet near the periscope. Visitors looking into the lens at eye level can experience seeing a signal as the S&T staff would have done. S&T staff would have seen it, upside down.

The wooden top to the periscope (right) displays a marked similarity to the design of an actual signal lamp - as we might well expect for both designs would have emanated from the same S & T drawing office. There would likely have been several of these periscopes kept at different locations, for although marked 'Wimbledon', signal renewals, replacement and additions were an ongoing process as witness the number referred on the regular weekly notices. (The latter expected to be read by train crews so as to keep up to date.) In addition visits to site would occur if a signal were reported as being difficult to view. The Western Region and likely the other railways had a similar system although futher details have not yet emerged. We do know for example the (G)WR had a 'Signal Sighting Committee' whose members would visit locations where signal alterations were proposed and make the relevant notes; these subsequently passed to the installers. Any further information would be welcome.